THE CUCKOO PEN

TALES OF ENGLISH VILLAGE
LIFE BETWEEN THE WARS

DEDICATION

*I dedicate this book to the actors on life's stage called
The Cuckoo Pen, for without them there would be no story. The
Cuckoo Pen is a circle of beech trees on the hill where it is said
that our ancestors tried to keep the cuckoo impounded all the year
round to ensure perpetual summer.*

THE CUCKOO PEN

TALES OF ENGLISH VILLAGE
LIFE BETWEEN THE WARS

FRED ARCHER

Budding
BOOKS

First published in 1995 by
Alan Sutton Publishing Limited, an imprint of Sutton Publishing

This edition published in 1997 by Budding Books, an imprint of
Sutton Publishing Limited · Phoenix Mill · Thrupp · Stroud ·
Gloucestershire

British Library Cataloguing in Publication Data

Archer, Fred
Cuckoo Pen: Tales of English Village Life
Between the Wars
I. Title
823.914 [F]

ISBN 1-84015-010-6

Typeset in 12/15 Garamond.
Typesetting and origination by
Alan Sutton Publishing Limited.
Printed in Great Britain by
WBC Limited, Bridgend.

CONTENTS

ILLUSTRATIONS

INTRODUCTION

In *Under Milk Wood* Dylan Thomas wrote these words: 'If you have lived in one village you have lived in the lot'. How true that is. So often people say to me about some of my characters, 'We've got a chap in our village like Sacco.' Amy from Coney Burrows was our Polly Garter. (Don't be too hard on Amy, her mother Flora, Becky, or Olive; they were a comfort to so many at The Cuckoo Pen.)

The folk in this book really existed in the 1920s and '30s. There are a few composite characters and the names are not their real names. I feel so privileged to have been a boy in the audience when the actors took their places on life's stage. Life on the farm was so different. It was hard but everyone took part. Men's voices were deep and mellow as they followed the plough or sang their carols.

The book does not, I hope, give a picture of 'Rural Bliss', for that would be false; life was hard, sometimes cruel. I have often been asked 'Was life in the country better or worse in the 1920s than it is now?' My answer is 'Neither. It was different.' In this book it's my aim to present a word picture of life on the land and in the village between the wars.

THE FARM WORKER

We know that since the Second World War 'big business', with all that it entails, has invaded the world of farming. Villages have become dormitories for the workers in the towns, and the agricultural way of life has been affected in many ways.

First of all the farmers in the past relied on the village blacksmith to make and repair implements, and the wheelwright to make and repair carts and wagons. Today tractors, implements and vehicles all come from the manufacturers. They soon become outdated – victims of a throw-away society.

New ideas born in the town on the drawing boards of college-trained folk result in six-furrow ploughs and huge combine harvesters. But the hedges have to be ripped up to make room for these massive machines. As the threshing machine replaced the men who threshed with the flail early in the nineteenth century, so the six-furrow plough has made so many ploughmen redundant. We know it makes sense financially and farming is big business, but things have gone too far.

The time has gone when a man could make a living milking twenty cows. Now, a stockman must have one hundred cows to milk to be profitable. Cows today give huge yields of milk where five gallons a day was considered good in the years between the wars. Despite this the beasts are threatened with hormone treatment for still greater yields. But heavy yielding cows don't last long. They burn themselves out.

While it is true that combine harvesters and six-furrow ploughs can work many acres in a day, the operators sit in air-conditioned cabins listening to radios or tape recorders and have lost the feel of the natural things around them.

As we become saddled with milk quotas and Set Aside, where up to 15 per cent of the land has to remain fallow, no wonder there is a harking back to the old days on the land.

It was not all good, however, for there was poverty in the villages. Families who fell on hard times through illness had to 'go on the parish' for relief. But look at the other side; I never saw families ejected from their homes, while today many with mortgages have experienced just that. And bills ensnare householders like an ever-tightening noose. Is life better or worse? Well, it's certainly different.

The average farm worker in the twenties earned thirty shillings, ninepence an hour overtime, and worked fifty-two hours a week. Many a man worked an allotment, growing produce for the home and for market. He kept a few fowls and maybe a pig. He paid no income tax but ninepence a week was deducted from his wage for insurance against illness. Some men joined a Friendly Society, investing a little money for help during times of sickness. Generally, though, the calls on the farm worker's wages were nowhere near so complex as today. He paid three shillings per week rent, but no rates – these were paid by the farmer. His heating would be fuelled by coal (with wood for fire lighting), paraffin, and later electricity.

He was relatively poor but there was a thriftiness among the workers which had to be seen to be believed. Quite a few men managed to save and bought second-hand motor bikes.

One thing which is very different today from the years between the wars is the lack of humour, innocent fun, among the workers. Everyone seems so serious and concerned mainly with money. When as a boy I first worked among the men on the land there was a great rapport between the old men and the boys, a feeling which both sides enjoyed at bait time under the hedgerow. We boys were always blamed for anything that went wrong. It was a recognized fact that a broken pitchfork, a gate left open allowing the cows to stray, a horse's sore shoulder, were all our fault.

As we had our bread and cheese and cold tea at 10 o'clock we, that is Frank, Geoff and I, used to say to old George the cowman, nicknamed Blenheim, 'You've got past it.' 'You chaps, the specials,' he replied, 'unt fit to be working along with us. You aught to be on some stage.' Mind you, we did sing to the old men. 'There ain't no sense sitting on the fence all by yourself in the moonlight' – a popular song of the time. But those old men – Blenheim and Jubilee – were as good as gold. They never let us down in front of the Gaffer, and whether hoeing the mangolds or singling the young plants they were without equal. We were green and often they helped us out at the end of the row. Unhurried, the work seemed to melt away.

After the back-breaking task of picking broad beans .and strawberries, plum picking was a treat. The Gaffer insisted that, first of all, we stayed on the ground and picked the fruit off the lower branches, while the men used ladders and picked the plums from higher in the trees. Then we were given light ladders of twenty rungs and were instructed how to set our ladders in the trees. That was fine but life can be boring without mischief and we were never short of that.

We put our ladders in the same tree as Blenheim and Jubilee and slanted the ladders towards their almost upright ones, thus making the job quite hazardous. When Old Jubilee had picked the whole tree and went to empty his basket of plums he discovered that we had tied his ladder to the tree. Pulling and snatching he shouted to me, 'I'll acquaint your father.' At that moment Dad was actually standing there and had a job to hide a smile, but said 'Now you boys, just get on with your work.'

Out in the hayfield work was a pleasure. It didn't matter how little we earned; Frank and I felt so fortunate to be working in the sunshine with Flower and Pleasant, raking up the hay into walleys (or wind-rows) for the pitcher. We rode on iron seats and thought it was wonderful, especially after the hard slog of the winter, when we had to pull our hobnailed boots out of the clinging clay.

The men who pitched the hay worked two walleys at a time, the wagon moved between these two rows of hay. Oh, we tried to rake an equal amount of hay into each walley but it didn't always work that way.

'Thus twice as much hay in my row than in Harry's,' Old Blenheim complained. 'You buoys got no idea and when Friday night comes you aught to be ashamed to hold your hand out for the money.'

As I drove Captain and Turpin from Didcot Ham to Gipsies Lane pulling a full load of hay the hub of the wagon just touched the gatepost and the wooden post, being partly rotten, fell across the gateway. 'Now what you done? You be no use nor ornament,' Harry shouted from the hayfield.

As I steered the horses and wagon up the lane to the rick-yard the overgrown hawthorn hedges combed the hay from the load leaving a trail of sweet-scented herbage along the roadside. The approach to the rick-yard was steep. I stayed at the entrance while one of the men who built the rick came and led the filler, the shaft horse, and with me holding Turpin we charged up that incline. As the rick got higher the elevator pole, known as the monkey pole, was erected with its swinging jib and menacing-looking forks. Here was magic unloading the wagons. I led Captain alongside the rick, pulling a rope which went through pulleys to the jib. When the forks were rammed into the hay, Dad, perched on the load, shouted 'Cup, cup, steady' and the forkful of hay swung across the rick. Dad pulled the trip cord, and the hay fell at the feet of the rick builder. For the forks to come down to wagon level Captain had to be backed. I have never known such a hard-mouthed animal as that ridge-backed gelding. He was strong, he could pull, but he was difficult to reverse. 'Let's have a bit more pudding,' Dad called from the load until Captain had given enough rope for the next load.

And so the ricks were built and, before thatching, they were pulled – all the loose hay was taken from the sides and the ends until the whole structure resembled a thatched cottage. There was a pride in rick building, and the men from different farms would compete against one another.

Conversations between men at that 10 o'clock snack time concentrated on the crops, the animals and the land. Men worked in close cooperation with their employer. Failed crops or disease among animals concerned them. Carters spoke of 'my horses' not the farmer's horses. When liver fluke killed hundreds of sheep one wet year in the 1920s the shepherd threatened to drown himself in the moat pond. It was no idle threat. He shed many tears over his flock. 'I don't mind carrying any of my tools except this 'ere spade,' he said one February day. Having to bury the diseased sheep was a double blow to him, he knew them individually. Lambs died with pulpy kidney disease, and worst of all lamb dysentery. Today, we must give praise to the scientists for producing vaccines to prevent so many animal diseases.

The land was another subject ever in the mind of master and man. It seemed as if they loved the land, and that it loved them when the clay clung so lovingly to their boots. Smallholders wouldn't even have a horse on their allotments; it was dug and cultivated the hard way. For larger areas, the horse and simple tackle was the only way to prepare the soil for cropping. Today, this tackle would appear primitive. After ploughing the land farmers depended on the winter frost to lax the clay, and produced a tilth by a couple of treatments with the duck foot drags, a heavy harrow with tines shaped like ducks' feet. To produce a fallow in summer the Larkworthy scuffle, pulled by four horses, moved clods of earth our carter described as being as 'big as 'osses yuds'.

Consider the implements of today. First of all disc harrows pulled by tractor will produce a tilth after going over the ground several times. The speed of the tractor and the off-setting of the discs are magic. The Rotovator chops up the soil, the weeds, sprout stems, taking the backache out of cultivation. (I am speaking of the clay lands of the Midlands where the plough cut the land like rashers of bacon, an unbroken furrow from headland to headland. Light land farmers wouldn't know how to cope with such conditions. They work their land the next day after heavy rains; the clay land men have to wait until it's fit to go on their fields.)

So the men used to debate at bait time the best way to treat the land. They spoke of their potato crop, an important part of cottage economy, growing on the headlands of the farmer's field. The question was 'How's your taters?' They couldn't afford Scotch Seed, they swapped their tubers with neighbours from the other side of the village. New varieties did appear on allotments, just a few potatoes gathered from the farmer's clamp.

'We got a new sort of tater,' Harry, the carter announced in the Plough and Harrow, 'and he's a good un. I can't remember the name.'

One customer said 'Catriona', another suggested 'Arron Banner'.

'No,' Harry replied, 'that ain't it.'

Then 'Rhode Island Red' was mentioned and Harry said: 'That's it, that's the very name.'

Harry worked in the Doctor's garden in his spare time. The Doctor told him to put the potatoes farther apart in the row to give them more room.

'They are bound to be far enough apart, Doctor,' Harry said. 'I've planted some in your garden and some in mine.'

'How's your taters?' was a friendly question to the farm workers but if two men fell out a sort of curse was, 'I hope your taters get frosted'. What a threat.

LEISURE AND PLEASURE

As folk speed through the village today at the accepted thirty miles per hour (or more) the chat over the garden gate seems just a memory. The village street in the 1920s was almost free of motor traffic, and alive with men and women going to and fro from work. Stocky, the hurdle maker, with his game leg, propelled himself with an ash plant to and from Church. Harry, the carter, came past our house in the winter twilight, sparks flying from his hobnails as he scuffed the road to get them clean before going to his cottage. On those winter evenings Harry carried a log for his fire; to rest in the inglenook was a respite for him after a hard day behind the plough.

Hearing the thump, thump, thump of Arthur's wooden leg as he made his way home from the whist drive was a regular Wednesday night experience for me lying in bed under the eaves of our farmhouse. A versatile man was Arthur, he rode a motor bike, he picked apples from a ladder, and he stood in as goalkeeper in a friendly match for the village team. Blenheim, too, had an arthritic walk, a nautical roll from side to side, taking half the road. No one talked of being disabled in those days, when physiotherapy was an unknown science.

Stodge, who had been cutting the grass verges and shovelling up the muck from Harry's team and Blenheim's cows, lived one village away. As he walked home the blackbird in the hedge said, 'Stick it Stodge. Stick it Stodge.' He carried his frail basket and empty cider bottle the 2 mile journey home. The barrow Stodge used served two purposes; to wheel away the manure and for him to sit on over his midday dinner.

When the hurdy-gurdy man came, as he did every month, playing tunes by the village cross, Stodge was cutting the roadside verge. I said, 'How do you like the music, Stodge?' The reply came back, 'I'd sooner have it along with my fittle [food].'

Sacco was another who passed our house. To see him en route to Chapel on Sunday nights was a picture. Smart, no wonder the girls fell for him. He was dressed immaculately in a navy blue blazer, a bow-tie, a white shirt, Oxford bag trousers, black shoes with patent leather toecaps. Sacco was an athlete, a goalkeeper who could swing from the crossbar between the posts.

Tustin rode his bicycle through the village to football matches. What a price he paid for that liberty! Queenie insisted that on wet days that bike had to be cleaned and polished thoroughly before he had his tea. When the weather was fine he was allowed to run over the frame with an oily rag, then sling the bike off the floor on to one of the beams in the cottage, preserving the tyres. It's said that on one wet day at a football match Tustin covered his bike with his overcoat and got wet through himself. His bike was the envy of many a working man of The Cuckoo Pen. The majority of those who took to the lanes and the road in those days had to be content with rusty throw-outs of the gentry. But the urge to get away, to always be in a different town or village, had not arrived. It was a stay-at-home society, a make-do-and-mend era. The village would turn out en bloc for a cup-tie when its team took part in the match, but very few ventured to Birmingham to see Aston Villa.

One can never quite recapture the tenor of village life as it was in the 1920s. There was a relaxation difficult to describe. The hill around The Cuckoo Pen and Coney Burrows was a playground for the young, where Sunday afternoon sweethearting was part of life, and where the awareness of intimacy between sexes was natural. Not the what you might call bed romping seen on television nowadays, but an innocent closeness of couples which lay between platonic and full commitment. It's true some of the young villagers did 'slip up', as it were, but surprisingly few.

The older native villagers knew the footpaths over the hill from The Cuckoo Pen to Parsons Folly, from Benedict's Pool to Cobblers Quar, but on those hill fields early in this century no harm could be done by walking where one pleased. It was as if the hill was a back garden to one and all, and a source of food for free – ketchup mushrooms, blackberries and blueberries. No one cared if a rabbit was poached. The farmers were so overrun with them that they often allowed the labourers to go rabbiting. The close-cropped grass on the hill was not caused by cattle and sheep grazing there but by those pesky creatures. Stodge and Whistler, who were neither Church nor Chapel, sat in hides on Sunday mornings blasting away at another nuisance, pigeons, that plagued the many acres of sprouts on Dunn's land.

Another feature of the hill to me was the flowering every summer of the massive boar thistle. It gave a glow of purple and stood soldier-like, noisy with bees in summer, and with the chatter of goldfinches every autumn as they fed on the seed.

The countryside can be noisy today, but with tractors, combine harvesters, and silage cutters. Hark back to the four-horse team at plough; listen to the creak of the harness, the snort of the horses, maybe the squeak of the plough wheels and a certain crunch when the ploughshare and mould-board turn the furrow. The plough boy cracks his whip. Cup, cup, the carter calls. How the team recognize the tone of the voices, whether they are pleased or annoyed. When the carter shouts from the plough tails 'Come on now' Captain, the filler, shakes his head. The boy cracks his whip and the carter says, 'Don't thee hit that hoss. We don't want weals on his ass. Just speak to him sharpish.'

The age-old noises, the scents and smells of a countryside before the tractor urbanized the land and nitrate-grown silage was parcelled in plastic, black and enormous, are but a memory.

The Men and Women of The Cuckoo Pen

Amy

Amy was what Old Jubilee described as 'warm'; what a Madonna, with her golden tresses on her shoulders. Her peach-like complexion needed no artificial help, and her disarming blue eyes and bust made many a man look twice as she stood behind the bar at the Railway Inn. And she had dress sense.

Now, this girl could have married some business gentleman and lived a life of bliss. But no, Amy liked to play the field. Some of her escorts were just the run-of-the-mill folk of the Vale. Sacco, God bless him, heard the gorse pods pop on Coney Burrows as they made love, while Flora sang the hymns of Moody and Sankey at Chapel. A local builder was said to be madly in love with Amy. This chap knew where Amy's bedroom was, took a ladder and climbed through the window. When he came down the ladder the local policeman was at the bottom. No charges were made but I gather the constable was a bit jealous.

During the war Amy worked as receptionist at a hotel in town. She became involved with a black American soldier who had deserted from his company. Amy kept him hidden away in a wardrobe of her bedroom until he was discovered by the Military Police. Before or since, no one like Amy has ever walked the lanes and footpaths of The Cuckoo Pen.

Bunch and Cyril, the Churchwarden

Milly Bostock, known as Bunch, was often misunderstood. She was the 'Social Service' of the 1920s. No one in The Cuckoo Pen went hungry – Bunch provided. No one died of hypothermia – Bunch sent the coalman round.

Bunch had many so-called romances in her time. I listened to her tales of love as she paid her rent quarterly to my father. No soap opera could compare with her love stories; how, for example, the brass-hatted head of the fire brigade had wooed her. At one time a marriage between Bunch and Cyril, the churchwarden, looked likely. There was a love–hate relationship between the bachelor (a retired insurance man) and this descendant of the Baldwyn Squires.

Bunch planted daffodils on the roadside verge and gave Stodge, the roadman, glasses of wine to persuade him to respect the blooms with his scythe. On the other hand Cyril hacked away at the path through the churchyard with his stock-axe until Bunch declared there was room for a charabanc to travel between the graves. The mounds over the graves, thrown up and turfed by Cyril, were described by Bunch as marrow beds.

I can't see anyone today doing the amount of voluntary work. It wasn't always appreciated. Cyril paid for a man to mow the churchyard out of his own pocket.

FLORA

The Cuckoo Pen would not have been the same without Flora and Amy. Their asbestos bungalow at Coney Burrows overlooked the village. It stood in a spot surrounded by gorse, with fox earths and badger setts in the adjoining wood. Flora was nervous up there when Caleb, the blacksmith, was away visiting his family in the Forest of Dean. It was a hard life for this middle-aged woman who had buried her husband and two sons, all killed by the dreaded consumption.

She fetched her drinking water from a standpipe way down in the village, and she hauled paraffin, bread and groceries back up to Coney Burrows. Her two youngest children were still at school, little George and Patricia.

Flora liked to unload her troubles on to me. On one occasion she had been to the Doctor. He had prescribed some medicine for her, and then asked, 'Have you any more to tell me?'

Flora replied, 'Yes, Doctor. I don't sleep.'

'Why don't you sleep?'

'Why, I hear noises in the bushes in the gorse. I put my fingers in my ears and I sweat thinking that someone will come from the bushes and say, "Now I've got ya". Then I think how silly I am, God will take care of me. The children sleep, Doctor. I've had so much trouble.'

When she was banned from the Mothers' Union because of her association with Caleb she attended Chapel. But then Caleb left her, poor Flora, and she survived for a while on what was known as parish relief. Tom Dunn did his best as Guardian of the Poor to help this unfortunate widow, but when his wife asked him if he would like to go and see the operetta 'Flora Dora' that was too much. He had had enough Flora.

So Flora's lament was a tale which never ended. She was a handsome widow, dressed in cast-offs from the Manor but always with that black band of ribbon around her neck. She was a wonderful writer of begging letters too, always with the PS: My size in shoes is 6.

Coney Burrows is different today. The bungalow has fallen down but the gorse still thrives, blossoming from Christmas Day to Christmas Day.

HARRY

Dunn's carter, Harry, was a little man who worshipped his horses. He was also a rick builder, a rick thatcher, a ploughman, etc. With permanently raised eyebrows as if surprised, he stole cattle cake for his horses. He dressed in Cyril Pumphrey's cast-offs and was known to follow the plough in plus-fours. He kept lots of boots in the harness room and suffered with his feet. He cut holes in the uppers to ease his corns. Harry would smoke anything, cigarettes, cigars and his pipe. If he ran out of tobacco when he was ploughing at the headland he would chat up any stranger who happened to come along the road, saying: 'I suppose you an't got a cigarette or some tobacco.' When he was offered the tobacco pouch he would produce a big cherry pipe from his jacket and fill the bowl. Lighting up he would say: 'Thank you sir. I an't had a wift of tobacco all day.' The ploughing went so much better then and, douting the pipe for a few bouts with the plough, Harry would sing his songs. A good-tempered man, except on some Saturday afternoons when he'd drunk too much of Laughing Tom's cider, Harry was one of the best at pitching and loading hay in The Cuckoo Pen meadows.

GEORGE

Dunn's cowman, known as Blenheim, was a man who could trace his ancestors back to the Commonwealth. An arthritic chap with a cutting sense of humour, Blenheim propelled himself along behind his herd of cows with an ash plant. His walk was not exactly a nautical roll but a swaying from side to side which became familiar to us all. Blenheim never married and lived in a thatched cottage up a lane known as Bachelor's Avenue because so many like him lived there. Unshaven but with a bristly grey whiskered chin rather than a beard, he was dressed winter and summer in heavy corduroy trousers with a fall front, a front with buttons either side which when undone came down like the tailboard of a wagon. He wore an Oxford shirt, the uniform of farm men in that day, covered by what was known as a slop, a light cotton jacket. His hobnailed boots and the thump of his ash plant in the rough lane marked time, one two three, one two three.

One winter night as he drove his little herd up Gipsies Lane Bridy, the Alderney cow, ran amok under Olive's drooping ash tree. Only then did Blenheim's pace change from a leisurely ambling stroll to a painful short charge, his hobnails making sparks as he chased the runaway shouting 'Damn you Bridy. I'll strike you like Moses struck the rock when he was with the Children of Israel.' A proud man, when old age and infirmity got the better of him, Blenheim refused to 'go on the parish' and lived on his ten shillings a week pension until Tom Dunn persuaded him to accept some relief.

MISS JEFFREYS

This retired nurse from a London Hospital arrived at The Cuckoo Pen soon after the First World War. A lean angular figure, she lived with a rather masculine, shortish violinist named Hilda, who was resplendent in tweeds, with a white shirt and bow-tie.

'What Phyllis Jeffreys knew and what she didn't know was a hell of a lot,' Blenheim remarked. She had nursed with farming families since leaving London and claimed to know more about cows, horses and other farm animals than the native sons of The Cuckoo Pen. As an ardent supporter of the RSPCA I was concerned when Miss Jeffreys became a Local Secretary of the association, knowing that she would create problems at The Cuckoo Pen.

An Exmoor pony with a coat like a rug, owned by a farmer, grazed next to her orchard. Miss Jeffreys maintained that it should be stabled in the winter. The pony was well fed with hay and in good condition. Even so, packets of Quaker Oats were put over the fence from her orchard, making the pony very frisky and it bolted with its young rider. That was quite a minor niggling event, but the farming of The Cuckoo Pen was much more serious.

I was rearing calves with a suckler herd of cows. The normal practice was to put three week-old calves on to a freshly calved cow, who suckled them for three months. Then two calves were substituted and wean the three. They stayed for three months. By then the milk supply of the cow would only be enough to rear one calf. It was early summer and when my cows had taken to the one calf I decided to turn the cows and calves out into my fields. This saved me the trouble of bringing the cows to the cowshed morning and night to have the calves suckled there. The other cows and the calves did remarkably well that summer, but as autumn came it was necessary to bring the calves into the barn and wean them there. These calves had not been having a great deal of milk for by then the cows were in calf and becoming dry. The calves were lug tits. The cows dried off grazing my orchard. The calves in the barn bawled until they were hoarse for several days. It's a natural thing when they are weaned. Jack, my cowman, fed them on hay and cattle cake.

Then I had a phone call from Miss Jeffreys, who threatened me with these words, 'Your man is not feeding the calves properly. I can hear them calling and I shall report you to the RSPCA.'

I was flabbergasted and replied, 'Will you give me their phone number?' This she did.

I rang the officer who told me that if she reported me they would have to come out. The officer and the policeman came the next day, examined the cows and calves, and complimented me on their condition. I told them what I was feeding them on and he replied, 'If you are giving them newspaper to eat, continue with it. I've never seen a better bunch of calves.'

The local branch had many unjustified complaints from Miss Jeffreys. Eventually she was relieved of the Secretaryship, but not before other folk of The Cuckoo Pen had been troubled.

JOE AND LOFTY

Compared with the Pennys, Joe and Lofty were in a league of their own in the market gardening world. William and Robert tinkered, planted their crops meticulously, in straight rows, grooming the land. Joe and Lofty, Chapel elders, kept to their ancient calendar, planting on Saints' Days, wheeling the manure from their pigsties and digging it into their land. Great heaps of household soot stood on the headland. The land was cared for, but there was a certain untidiness around their patch, where the tools of yesterday were still in use. They breast ploughed the bean stubble and seemed to have fires of squitch (couch grass) all the year round. Their holding of 12 acres was three times as large as William and Robert Penny's. The land was dug, raked and hoed the hard way. They did keep a donkey to transport the produce to the local station and on occasions to the local market. I have memories of their donkey in the market in the town giving voice to others. The braying drowned the auctioneer's voice. Neddy started and then the whole chorus joined in.

The two gardeners dug their clay land with two-pronged, or two-tined, forks. They wore foot irons over their hobnailed boots to protect the soles. Digging in rhythm, the clank of the foot irons could be heard from the lane. Poetry in motion.

The visiting seedsman from well-known merchants did good business with William Penny but not with Joe and Lofty. These men seeded their own sprouts, wallflowers, cabbages, beans, etc., selecting the best stems for their seed. A very early strain of wallflower seed gave Joe and Lofty blooms for market a couple of weeks earlier than their neighbours.

They kept the Sabbath as strictly as in the Highlands of Scotland. Nothing happened on Sunday apart from the three services at the Chapel. The vegetables for Sunday dinner had been picked and prepared on Saturday night, enough to last until Monday morning. The boots were blackened on Saturday. On the holding, the starlings could be feasting on the strawberries, the crows on the peas, but on a Sunday Joe and Lofty would be talking to God.

When Joe preached to the little knot of villagers he emphasized that the hard work, the hard life, was just a sort of overture to the life to come; that the New Jerusalem was worth all the hardship, the pain, of the world. There were little quips in Joe's prayers which often came from his favourite hymns – 'Here from the world we turn Jesus to seek'. He endeavoured to divorce worship completely from everyday life. His sermons, if they could be called that, were punctuated with 'What did the Postle Paul say?' Then followed a reading from one of Paul's letters. And after that, 'What does the Poet say?' and a few lines from a hymn.

At one time, after a late frost had spoiled their crops, many market gardeners were drowning their sorrows with home-made plum wine, plum jerkum. Not so our two Chapel elders. When the Vicar questioned them, asking 'How will you two men live?', the reply came back, 'The ravens fed Elisha. There's always next year if we are spared.'

OLIVE BECKFORD

Known as the Merry Widow, Olive was the daughter of a Superintendent of Police and married Fred Beckford, a prosperous farmer. Unfortunately Fred died soon after Olive's daughters were born. She was a beautiful woman living in the farmhouse where Fred had farmed, and as an ex-nurse she cared for the poor folk of The Cuckoo Pen.

It seemed that Olive also fulfilled a need among the widowers and bachelors of the parish, although to say that she was promiscuous would be rather unkind. The ladies of The Cuckoo Pen got very worried if their husbands spent time at Olive's farm, but she always chose those who were unattached. Old Snob, the shoemaker, was diagnosed by Doctor Overthrow as 'overdoing his nature' with Olive Beckford. Perhaps her favourite suitor was a chap from the Cotswolds named Gifford. When he died, Olive threw a rose on to his coffin and said: 'He was the only man any good to me.'

She looked a picture when she went off to Cheltenham in her governess car pulled by a jet-black cob with silver-mounted harness – the Boudicca of The Cuckoo Pen. In the days before make-up was commonplace, her face was marbled with cream and powder and her lips were poppy red. Olive had style.

During the hot summer of 1926, and the railway strike, Olive would drive her cob to town, but cycle round the village announcing to Dunn's farm men that it was so hot she had no knickers on. 'Thurs temptation,' Old Blenheim said. 'That's a fact. Thurs temptation.'

She treated her lovers with kindness, gave her cast-off clothes and shoes to poor Flora and massaged Blenheim's game leg. Olive was a good-hearted woman and part of the way of life around The Cuckoo Pen.

SACCO, MILKO AND THE DOCTOR

Although misfits of society these three characters did add colour to life at The Cuckoo Pen.

Sacco was the athletic mason and plasterer, game for anything, amusing and what Blenheim described as 'gallus'. Sacco, who followed Stocky as grave-digger, also made tombstones from granite chippings for folk who couldn't afford the stonemason's charges. They were works of art, apart from the fact that sometimes the names of the deceased had to be abbreviated to fit the words on the stone.

Sacco and Milko were great friends. On those Saturdays when the pair drove to Cheltenham in Milko's open tourer it was a sight to behold. The car, a Britain, with wooden spoked wheels, brass headlamps, brass sidelights, a Klaxon horn, befitted their characters. King Edward VII looked no more regal than these two from The Cuckoo Pen.

Sacco was always a tidy man at work or leisure. On Saturdays in the car with Milko he was splendid in a navy blazer, white shirt, coloured bow-tie and silver-grey Oxford bags. And although Milko rarely washed and spent the week ankle deep in cow muck, he too made an effort on those Saturday excursions. An Eton collar, a Norfolk jacket and cavalry twill trousers changed the man into an aristocratic gentleman, a descendant of the Squire.

These trips to town were often arranged when The Cuckoo Pen Football team had an away match there. They supported The Tigers, so called because of their gold and black strip. After the match Sacco and Milko had dinner at a classy restaurant in the Promenade, then went to the Full Moon in Lower Dockham, Lower High Street. Here they drank deeply of the local ale, and were duly entertained by the Tarts of Dockham. The Britain conveyed our two playboys back to The Cuckoo Pen in the early hours of Sunday morning, and the muddled milkman, after changing into his work clothes, milked the red Rubies in lantern light.

The aristocratic nature of Milko's car, a rare breed I gather, was further endorsed on the occasions it was used by the Overthrow family. Doctor Overthrow would sit beside his son; Milko would be the chauffeur. The Doctor was Victorian to the core. He wore a frock-coat, a cravat, a box hat, tightly tailored trousers, spats and button-up boots. His clipped Edward VII type beard below his well tobacco-stained moustache showed him to be a professional gentleman.

The Doctor used his high trap, pulled by his horse Lavender, to make his village visits and to get to the station where he would board the train for town. Meanwhile, Milko, a rather undependable chauffeur, would lie in bed during the day, milking his cows at midnight.

TEDDY PRIDE, OR MONKEY BRAND, AND HIS WELL-ENDOWED WIFE

Teddy and his wife Pamela lived in a three-storey house at the top of The Cuckoo Pen. He had been a farmer of sorts but marrying late, when he was fifty-two, to a moneyed lady gave them both independence. Mrs Pamela Pride, well named, stood head and shoulders above her husband. Teddy was, as Sacco would say, only five foot and a tater. His little face was encircled with ginger whiskers, and ginger hair peeped from under his black bowler hat.

He was a timid man exploited by the Church and the Mothers' Union. 'Oh, yes,' they would say, 'Teddy will carry the water from the standpipe to the Church Hall'; 'Teddy will pin the notices to the shed by the cross advertising the Lantern Lecture'. In the house poor Teddy blackleaded grates, scrubbed floors, peeled potatoes, washed the dishes. But in a way Teddy enjoyed being a dogsbody. When he did need to get away, his orchard, prolific with fruit and noisy with fowls, gleanies and geese, provided an oasis.

Pamela had lived at The Manor with her parents, waited on hand, foot and finger. As far as men were concerned, she could be described as a 'Stone Waller'. Teddy's cousin Joe courted her for a while, but Joe was clumsy, forward, not acceptable to Pamela. His words to me were amusing: 'I was having a bit of a cuddle along with Pamela and was just getting towards the promised land when she gave me the master smack on the nose.' What a contrast to Teddy, such a little gentleman. So we have this couple yolked together, yet happy, for any decisions were made by Mrs Pride and Teddy acquiesced.

A picture comes vividly to mind of these Victorians walking tandem to Church on Sunday mornings. Pamela walked sedately in front, upright, big bosomed, dressed in navy shot-silk with jewellery around her neck and pinned to her breast. She held her head up high and carried her prayer books. Two paces behind came little Teddy, Monkey Brand, following this grand lady, who could have been a duchess, and him, a little pillar of the Church, dwarfed by his gorgeous wife. Teddy looked down at the feet of Pamela, watching his step so that the two paces between him and his wife remained constant. How Mrs Pride and Teddy made a match of it one can only speculate.

Mrs Pride stood out as a guardian of Teddy and the orchards. No one argued with her. There was some friction between her and Bunch. You see, Bunch was very proud of her heritage and frequently reminded the folk of The Cuckoo Pen that her family could be traced back 500 years. Be that as it may, the last of Bunch's family to be Lord of the Manor died over twenty years ago. Since then Mrs Pride, as a spinster, had lived in The Manor.

Mrs Pride, who was never a mother nor likely to be after a late marriage, was a regular member of the Mothers' Union. Why shouldn't she be, for the president was Bunch, who never even married. I never saw Mrs Pride except when she was dressed for meetings. The stately walk to Church impressed me but as a boy I thought it frightening. Her outsize body looked like a Worcester porcelain vase ornamented with gold and pearls. I talked with Teddy when he was sawing logs for the fire in his orchard of Blenheim and Warners King apples. He wore a butcher's apron over his jacket and moleskin trousers, his bowler hat was deep and green with age. Teddy was dressed for weekday work.

TOM DUNN

A leading light in the affairs of the village, Dunn was a farmer, parish councillor, district councillor, Chapel elder, on occasion a local preacher, and a good judge of cattle. He employed many casual workers in the summer, apart from his regular men.

REVD VERNON AND STOCKY, THE GRAVEDIGGER

Revd Vernon could be described as a good country parson, a man of the people. He worked with the Chapel on many occasions. He was without equal when it came to conducting funerals. However a man had lived, Revd Vernon found something good to say about him. While contemplating what to say to the mourners Revd Vernon would purse his lips in an interesting way.

For some years Stocky had told the Parson that they needed some new webbing to lower coffins into The Cuckoo Pen clay. Revd Vernon ignored this and when Auntie Phoebe was buried it happened! As the coffin was lowered the webbing broke and poor Auntie Phoebe was pitched into the grave more vertical than horizontal. After the funeral it took the bearers some time to put the coffin straight in the bottom of the grave.

Stocky never bothered to get a bit of fine soil to drop on the coffin. When the Parson said, 'Dust to dust, ashes to ashes' large lumps of clay resounded on the woodwork. A noisy farewell.

During one funeral the Parson had said such nice words about the woman he was burying. After most of the mourners had gone and there were just a few of us around Stocky said, in a stage whisper, 'Her's been a nice beauty in her time.'

Revd Vernon was a careful character and able to cope with all the niceties of The Cuckoo Pen. He and his son shared a bike between them. On Sunday mornings the son rode the bike halfway from a neighbouring parish 2½ miles away, leaving it under the hedge. Revd Vernon walked the first half and then picked up the bike and rode it to Church, his son walked the second half.

Revd Vernon was essentially a good man. He lived to be a hundred and two, and declared to a newspaper reporter that he attributed his long life to fish and chips with plenty of salt and vinegar. A hundred and two was a good innings.

WILLIAM AND ROBERT PENNY

William and Robert Penny came to The Cuckoo Pen as gardeners, working at The Close for a Birmingham gentleman whose business was in fish hooks. When he died, the gentleman was buried in the churchyard of St Luke's with a grand headstone, his grave fenced with iron bars.

When his employer died William took a smallholding in a field known as Ayles Acre. He was a musical man with a tenor voice. He sang in the Church choir. He would take a tuning fork to concerts to get the right note for his songs, old ballads which brought tears to the eyes of ladies. He sang military pieces too, like 'The March of the Cameron Men'. He was a cultured man of the city, educated at the Cathedral School.

The smallholding was treated as a gentleman's garden by William and his son, Robert. They lived on that 4 acres and after some years of work, no weed dared to grow on the Ayles Acre Plot. The Pennys' neighbour, Tat Steward, the one-eyed husband of Mrs Steward who did the villagers' washing, neglected his holding. The thistles and docks grew high among his plum trees. Penny was continually watching Steward's plot, cutting down seeding thistles before the thistledown blew across on to his holding.

It's Sod's Law that when land is cultivated and kept free of weeds, then some other blight will strike. That year, a frost came in the late spring killing the Pennys' plums, but on Tat Steward's land, where the weeds grew up among the trees, there was a bumper crop. Maybe the weeds took the morning frost and protected the blossoms. The most likely reason was that Tat's holding was on a higher plain than the Pennys' and frost settles, like water, on low ground.

THE CUCKOO PEN:
A MIDSUMMER'S DAY

It was Sunday midnight, the fields drenched with dew and moonlight. Joe and Lofty trudged through the June grass towards the dim outline of die-straight beds of asparagus. Chapel hymns still rang through their muffled, cloth-capped heads. The sparrow-grass stood, soldier-like and budded. It remained uncut on Sunday because Joe and Lofty kept the Sabbath free from the asparagus knife, free from everything, free apart from their Sunday dinner and a pig-prodding, hair-cutting morning. At afternoon Chapel, in pitchpine pews, the preacher spoke of a better land if they kept the rules. What were the rules? Not to cut sparrow-grass or over-ripe strawberries on Sundays.

Emma and Mercy, their two wives, sat on the strawberry headland, bonneted, hurden-aproned, on straw boltings, listening for the church clock and on the last stroke of twelve, when ordinary folk lay on flock mattresses dreaming, Emma nodded her head and groping with finger and thumb nail picked the over-ripe strawberries into punnets. It was Monday morning.

In the moonlit sparrow-grass Joe and Lofty worked silently, sliding steel-pronged knives under buds until the left hand felt the stems fracture under the clay beds. Each bud then was bunched like nut fire sticks, lying in the palms of their hands until their gnarled fingers could hold no more of the food of the rich. This was food for the stockbroker, the city merchant. What a queer life on the Midland clay, groping in moonbeams on a cold June night, striving to find the buds which had stood erect in blazing sun on Sunday afternoon. The preacher said SIX DAYS SHALT THOU LABOUR. To start before twelve would break the

Sabbath, would bring hell and damnation to all instead of the promise, THE BEST IS YET TO BE.

'I'd like the best now,' muttered Lofty. 'We be just two of many hundred fools in the Eversham Vale who have waited for midnight, in company with coughing and farting sheep in the meadow and the munch of milk cows twisting their tongues round the sodden grass, hooting owls, whistling of plovers, screaming of vixen. The produce of the land without the taint of Sunday harvested for Monday's market.'

The Preacher snored, dreaming of golden gates. His Sunday black trousers lay like two drainpipes on the straw-coloured ply-seated, auger-holed bedside chair. His coat hung on the door. Nothing stirred in his Holy of Holies but the tick, tick, tick of his half-hunter, alberted and chained in his waistcoat.

As Phoebus showed orange over the Cotswolds, streaks of four o'clock light beamed across the backs of the women, picking out white bonnets, hurden aprons, and rows of chipped strawberries drenched with dew. Alongside, Joe and Lofty walked once more the senseless avenues of Monday morning, cutting the missed bud, collecting the handfuls of gras into hampers. A mocking cuckoo, broken voiced in late June, strained cuck, cuck, ooo. The weighed strawberries, the tied asparagus were wheeled in a barrow to await the market cart.

'Cooop-cooop-cooop, come on,' George, the cowman, called his milkers. All except Ada, who bawled for her calf, were loath to leave the grass; there was nothing better in the stalls but George's monotonous tit lugging. Moo-oo, moo-oo, baa, moo-ou moo-ou, baa. George, ash plant in hand, swayed in a Monday-morning daze up the lane. George, who had not been three times to Bethel but just once to the Plough and Harrow. His yud, he said, punished him for his excess. 'Damn your pelt, into the stalls you occud lot of cow bags,' he shouted.

A puff of smoke from Farmer Dunn's chimmuck told the workers that he had put match to sticks and that the kettle swung on the pot-hook for another Monday morning cup of tea.

'Annie,' he shouted up the backstairs and down came the maid, hair-curlered, sleepy-eyed, to prepare Farmer Dunn's breakfast. 'Have you seen Harry with the horses yet?'

'No, Sir, he beunt yer it.'

Then in the distance they heard the clip-clop of Harry's haltered team. Harry whistled at the dawn chorus, a starling mocked him, a spark or two flew from the hooves of Violet the brood mare as she stepped gingerly over the Clee Hill stones. Harry's dog followed him, working the hedge for rabbits down the lane, not that a June rabbit would be any good but Rough did this daily search as sure as Harry led the team.

Chee, chaw, chee, chaw, the milk sang in George's pail. Ada mooed, George muttered, suffering from that half a gallon of cider at the Plough and Harrow. 'Thou blasted beast, it yunt the fust time you a bin confined.'

Shuffling into the hay house for fodder George stumbled over Sacco who had not quite got home. George swore at the heap of tweed and cord which should have been sleeping in the harness room.

'Good morning, George, I've got a grave to dig today. Fifteen bob. Not bad ay?'

As the crook-propelled shepherd came coughing and twist-spitting off the hill he shouted into the cowshed. 'Unt thur nobody as went to bed last night.'

Bang, bang, went Lofty's double-barrel gun as it emptied two black-ringed, black-powdered cartridges into the backsides of a drove of strawberry stealing starlings. 'In this Cuckoo Land thurs no more sleep, no rest for the wicked – nor the righteous,' the shepherd sighed.

Up at Coney Burrows Flora woke her family. 'Nobody remembers the way I was brought up. Gentlefolk we were, Father had a groom,' she whispered as she opened the door of the living room.

After breakfast her daughter Amy walked brazenly down the street to the Church. Going up the steps of the Bethel, she unlocked the vestry door where the bucket, the broom, the brush awaited her on Monday morning. She hummed a hymn and scrubbed the steps, dusted the table where last night the Lord's Supper was observed.

Amy smiled and thought, 'Oh, last night I was wicked. Sacco was wicked as he crept up Coney Burrows as the bell tolled for evensong and Flora walked through the gate. I met Sacco, wicked Sacco, lovely Sacco, he's nice before the cider gets him. Our Mother is no better than she should be, the Vicar says she's banned from the Mothers' Union. Got a lodger we have, with tattoos on his arms. Our Mum likes him, he's been a sailor. Oh this Chapel! What a mess they made last night. Yurs sixpence under the pulpit, I'm wicked but I'll still put him in the Mission Box. Sacco, I'll see you again Sunday.'

Farmer Dunn's ewes were already bunched up under the elms sheltering from the sun that brought the flies sizzling through the still air. They lay with snow-white fleeces, dew-wet bellies, chewing the cud and enjoying the short-lived cool.

Harry's two horses did the circuit of Pecked Meadow with the mower. The blade chattered in the fingers. Oil plastered everything, even the rope reins, as Harry sat on the iron-seated machine steering his course, leaving honey-scented swathes of herbage in kinky rows.

As the sun's rays got stronger, hotter and blistering, Boxer and Turpin kicked as the traces touched their hocks at the field corners. They kicked at the flies, Brees or Old Maids, laid their ears, and showed the whites of their eyes as Harry left the bridge of his grass cutting ship and smacked bare-handed the briskets of the beasts, slaughtering those Old Maid bloodsuckers, and tying elder flowers to bridles to ward off the pestilence.

Back at the smallholding Joe and Lofty had their breakfast, the sparrow-grass was cut, the strawberries picked. Joe fed his Monday-hungry pig, a pig which had not been fed on Sunday.

The Preacher said SIX DAYS SHALT THOU . . . but this Sunday the Sabbath had been broken. Broken by whom? Joe's Rhode Island cock had been seen by Church and Chapel Sunday-treading Joe's hens! Joe must pay for the crime. He killed the bird with a knife, hung him in Emma's wash-house where the steam rose from the copper. Blood dripped from the bird, sacrificed, into an enamel dish.

Revd Vernon called. 'Any idea where Sacco is this morning?'

'Oi, down in Dunn's cowshed. See how I tried to keep the Sabbath from defilement, Master Vernon?'

'What, by sacrificing your cockerel? How strange. Why Joe, why?'

''Cos he rode the hens isterday.'

'We no longer live under Old Testament law, Joe. But I must away and find Sacco.'

Sacco was back in the harness room, frying six eggs and four sausages for breakfast. Four sausages were fried but only three were sizzling in the pan and as the Parson entered, Sacco was on his knees looking for the lost sausage. Giving up he ate what remained of his breakfast. Slipping his foot into his Wellington he trod on and squashed the lost sausage as he wellingtoned his way to the standpipe tap.

'Funeral at two,' the Parson said. 'I'm busy today, it's a Saint's Day. I have a service at ten this morning.'

'I'll be in six foot by twelve, I got the measure of the grave,' Sacco replied.

Revd Vernon left and the postmistress, Cissy Treadwell, arrived with a letter for Sacco, a crossed stamped letter with kisses all over the envelope.

'Sacco,' Cissy said, 'were you and Amy among the gorse last night while Flora was at church?'

'I'm sixty-one and still potent and I hope to remain so,' Sacco said with a grin.

'You'll need to if that letter's from where I think. I know the postmark. I know the writing.'

Sacco's trembling fingers slid along the fold in the envelope. 'Ah, it's from Beckie Hampton. Listen, Ciss. "Dearest Sacco, I know you bury poor old Mrs Tomkins today, a happy release I would say. I'll walk to the funeral, be there about 1 o'clock outside the church tower. Do you think there would be time for a bit of slap and tickle in the grave before the funeral?" Go to hell! Amy Sunday, now Beckie. But I'm potent at sixty-one. I dig graves, I repair houses, dig gardens. I'm game, Cissy, I'm game.'

Cissie tittered down the yard from the harness room to spread the news to all the good women of what it said in Beckie's letter.

Cyril Pumphrey, a product of one of the then fashionable Birmingham suburbs, never quite fitted into The Cuckoo Pen. He was a retired insurance manager, described by Stodge the roadman as a pen-pusher. In fact, the bachelor brother-in-law of Revd Vernon tried to imitate Stodge, who worked on the village road, by making wide tarmac paths up the churchyard. He even used tools like the roadman, a stock axe and heavy spade.

But what an imitation of a countryman! A silver-banded walking stick, a silver-banded pipe and those ox-blood coloured brogues and the pepper-and-salt tweed suit; a sad man who fancied Milly Bostock but never won her affection. Stodge, in his corduroys, uneducated, coarse, delved deep into Cyril's tobacco pouch to fill his clay pipe and accepted the shilling on Fridays for sweeping the road to the lych-gate.

Together these two countrymen would stand on the football field on those winter Saturdays. Cyril was secretary of the Tigers, while Stodge lubricated the home team at half-time with cider from a great jar. He limped onto the pitch and each man had a drink from a cider horn. Two men, miles apart in education and manners, yet Stodge accepted the city man and spoke well of him in the pub.

On that nasal 'Morning', with raised trilby to all, Cyril arrived at the village cross where Milly Bostock passed with jam-jarred flowers for the Holy Table. Cyril borrowed Milly's broom to sweep the churchyard path and forgot to take it back. He did comment on Milly's flowers, but received only acid comments, sarcastic comments, in return.

Monkey Brand Pride at Hill View, hen-pecked by that large, big bosomed wife, seemed happy in his situation. It was a constant source of wonder in The Cuckoo Pen how this little ginger-bearded man was scooped up by the upright lady who came from the Manor.

To see Teddy Pride under petticoat government in the kitchen of Hill View created a sympathy among the folk of The Cuckoo Pen, but Teddy was happy beyond description. He had the support, the guidance of a very able woman. Mrs Pride's house was in today's parlance 'clinical'. Teddy was far superior to any charwoman in the village. Everything shone, from the kitchen to the oak staircase. To be true to Teddy, he had farmed and knew how to deal with their big garden, but he not only grew the potatoes and peas, but prepared them for cooking.

Sunday was always a Red Letter Day, Mrs Pride dressed in navy-blue shot-silk, a hat to match and its veil over her powdered face, walked to church tandem fashion, with Teddy behind, in his Sunday best with black bowler hat. Mrs Pride from the Manor was proud of her capture, and he happier than Cyril's unrequited love for Milly Bostock.

Jasper Hill had left his hurdle maker's bench, left the withy-splitting, ladder rung-making workshop to toll the bell for 10 o'clock, to light the candles, to douse the candles, to say Amen like a clerk should, and to stop noisy folk coming up the churchyard.

Cyril, still sitting on the cross, heard the bell, heard the creaking of the woodwork as it swung on its oak hangings.

Revd Vernon mopped his brow and puffed as he left his tricycle in Milly Bostock's garden. Scurrying Milly, armed with music, brushed past Cyril and Revd Vernon. 'Cyril,' she shouted. 'Come and blow my organ if you mean to, or would you let me pedal?'

Cyril sniffed, douted his pipe, and walked with her through the church porch.

Miss Jeffreys arrived just in time for the service and sat in the front, making eyes at the vicar. In the pew behind, Beckie (longing for a man, says Stodge) also beamed at Revd Vernon. A few more of the retired, including Flora, sprinkled the pews. Cyril started pumping till the regulator reached the mark on the organ end, and Milly Bostock played a hymn. Miss Jeffreys warbled like a hundred nightingales for the Vicar's sake. When the service was over, the Vicar and Cyril made peace with Milly over sherry in her cottage, and Cyril put back the broom.

Milko was as much a part of the village as The Cuckoo Pen itself. As this hymn-singing purveyor of milk worked during the night he was given the name of the Midnight Milkman. He would have been fool enough to try and capture the cuckoo and put him in a pen high up on the hill, but the ring of trees known as The Cuckoo Pen was only a mile from Milko's cowshed. Perhaps during those hours of darkness he had a sort of commune with nature the nine-to-five folk never knew. The tawny owl hooting in the tree behind Milko's osier bed promised him a fine day to follow. The rooks as they dived and rose like the swirl of autumn leaves meant that rain was on its way up the Severn Vale.

Milko needed no weather forecast, for the brie flies tormented his red Ruby cows, driving them through the meadows until they took refuge in Milko's green algae-covered pond. Here they stood knee-deep, until this blond, long-haired man of the night, dressed in a deerskin waistcoat, chained them to the manger and what he called 'drew the blessing'. His milk was rich and creamy, his pints generous, poured out to what was known as a Malvern Measure.

Milko's midnight trek to Blacksmith's Lane took him and his float, pulled by his patient nag, past the badger setts. On moonlit nights he saw the young at play. Sometimes it seemed that Milko alone had The Cuckoo Pen to himself. He crossed the branch railway line, and watched the banana train labouring up the incline to the next station. At Blacksmith's Lane the delivery round began, the everlasting Woodbine cigarette scenting the air. Next day at dinner time in the post office and shop Milko renewed his stock of cigarettes but he was not welcome there. The postmistress sprayed disinfectant as he left to allay that smell of stale dung which hung like a cloud in the little thatched office and shop.

What a transformation took place on those Saturday nights Milko spent in town with Sacco! Cleaned, washed, shaved, wearing a Norfolk jacket and Lovat trousers, his shirt crowned with a bright cravat and a gold tie-pin. Here was the real descendant of the Baldwyn Squires. Sacco did him proud, for his navy-blue blazer, silver-grey Oxford bags and gaudy bow-tie complimented the milkman's attire as they set off in the open car for town.

Milko's pockets were full of gold sovereigns, aged and black from Grandmother Baldwyn's desk, a treasure trove which Milko never really appreciated.

Sacco, a man of the world, said, 'Now look here my friend, the pub in Cheltenham and the theatre are eager to take your golden money. Come with me to Montpellier where they buy sovereigns and I do believe the current rate of exchange is forty-two shillings for one sovereign.'

At the shop in Montpellier Sacco did the talking and tried for forty-five shillings, but settled for forty-three.

Sacco remembered when Milko used to cross Pecked Meadow with his milk float and let the neighbour's cattle onto the main road. He had no right to take that way and the farmer locked the gate. Undeterred, Milko unhung the gate and still took that short cut to the village. A padlock on that end of the gate presented a problem but Milko smashed it with his axe, landing himself in court.

'You were a fool my friend,' Sacco told him, 'to pay the ten-pound fine in sovereigns. The clerk must have made a profit that day.'

Jack Antonio lived in Lower Dockham, the down-town area of Cheltenham. He sold flowers in the Promenade and ice-cream from the side-car of his motor bike. His two daughters were beautiful, Jack being Italian and married to a half-gipsy from the Forest of Dean. The two Saturday night visitors from The Cuckoo Pen wined and dined those two girls, and after that the theatre. One wonders whether they would have been so eager to share Milko's sovereigns if they had seen him on weekdays, the Midnight Milkman.

Tat Stewart and his wife lived in a one-up, one-down cottage at the top of Blacksmith's Lane. They reared an enormous family of children; where everyone slept is a mystery. Tat lost an eye hedgecutting for Farmer Dunn. His glass eye was often a problem; sometimes he put it in the right way but often it was just showing white. Thursa Stewart helped to keep the family by taking in washing. Her sheets on the long line down the narrow garden were blinding white, no detergent could have produced such perfection.

Tat, a sad figure, an old soldier from the First World War, worked for Farmer Dunn. To say that he was mentally retarded would be rather unkind. Tat was simply a product of the land. On Dunn's farm he was not trusted with skilled work, but Thursa mothered him, worshipped him even. He helped her turn the big mangle when she was up to her eyes in laundry. It was common knowledge in The Cuckoo Pen that Gipsy Loveridge lopped the small young shoots of Farmer Dunn's withy trees, and he and the family made the white clothes pegs with bands from cocoa tins and sold them to Thursa Stewart.

In the long hot summers at The Cuckoo Pen the population doubled when the pea-pickers came. First, it was just a trickle of tramps who took up their sleeping quarters in Dunn's barns, pigsties and cart sheds. These were the men who came every year, claiming their places as of their right. Wisdom Loveridge and his family camped out in igloo-like tents, while the grandfather and grandmother slept in their hooped caravan. The mixture of humanity left the villagers puzzled as to where they all came from. Some had prams loaded with just a few possessions.

Soon folk from Lower Dockham, the area of Cheltenham near the gasworks, brought their whole families, a summer holiday with Grandad and Grandma, their sons and daughters and their children.

The travellers sat outside the Plough and Harrow singing until closing time on those Friday nights. Wisdom was always at hand, holding court outside the inn, or picking the early morning mushrooms on the hill and selling them to Cyril and the Vicar. He was there that time when Sacco fell from his bike and burst a bottle of cider that was in his pocket.

The flies buzzed around Sacco in the churchyard as he heard the eager Beckie walk up the gravel path to the back of the tower.

'Bit risky down in the grave,' he told her. 'Better amongst the elder on Canks Bank. No flies, no disturbance, a bed of ferns and bracken.'

Beckie wiped her glasses, mopped her forty-year-old brow, hitched up her skirt as Sacco's blue eyes looked more wicked than ever, yet kinder than ever.

'Twenty years I went without a man, lost at sea he was in the Marines.'

'You won't be disappointed, Beckie. We'll away to Canks Bank, the home of badgers, grey squirrels, jays, where the rabbit thumps in the underground burrows, and the cuckoo is calling.'

'Do you think Canks Bank was made for you and me to make love, Sacco?'

'Maybe' he said and they disappeared into the bushes.

At a quarter to two Stocky passed the funeral bell for Mrs Tomkins, and Beckie left Sacco and sat on the cross. At the foot of the church tower, just inside the belfry door, Sacco met Stocky.

'Ast got that ole out ett?'

Sacco was ready for Stocky's questions. He winked as he discarded his clay-stained jacket and shirt and took a clean shirt out of the drawer in the little ante room next to the vestry.

'I'm a carrying today.'

'Thee ut a have to look slippy,' Stocky continued.

As quick as it took Stocky to pull three or four pulls on the bell rope Sacco emerged in black suit, bow-tie and black boots, scurrying up the road where three more village men were outside Mrs Tomkins' cottage with the bier. With their doffed caps they entered and met undertaker Gregory, then spoke to his rein-tied pony hitched in the trap to the walnut tree. Reverently the four men manoeuvred Mrs Tomkins' remains down the steep, crooked stairs and placed the box on the bier. Gregory, top-hatted and with black gloves, solemn as a judge (an expression learned after years of this sort of thing), and upright, with arms slightly swinging, preceded the four men of The Cuckoo Pen as they wheeled the bier. As the flower-smothered carriage crept down the street, all the curtains were drawn at the cottage windows, men stood with horses or dogs and with their children, bare headed, holding their workaday caps in respect for Mrs Tomkins. At the church yew tree (the big one) Revd Vernon met the little procession. The mourners walked arm in arm behind the bearers. Stocky pulled the bell rope more often, until at last he stopped.

'Man that is born of woman hath but a short time to live and his life is full of misery,' Vernon chanted as they entered the porch.

Sacco thought, 'It unt all misery.'

Beckie thought, 'Sacco sixty-one and potent, hope he'll remain so.'

The pews filled up with the retired, the aged, the widows, the usual funeral addicts. Milly Bostock nodded to Cyril for wind for the organ. After the usual tradition, she murdered the Dead March in Saul, the bottom notes thundered through the chancel, resonating flower vases, spine-chilling the delicate, and annoying the musical.

Then out in God's acre among the yew, the laurel, the green berrying holly, Sarah Tomkins was lowered six foot into the blue clay. The interested, the sorrowful and the inquisitive, read the coffin plate: 'Sarah Tomkins, aged 81 years.'

Back at the cottage the family provided the feast. Sacco ate fish-paste sandwiches two at a time, drank the Chapel-urned tea, ate plum cake, and whispered to the other men in dark suits. 'It unt like it used to be years ago, we allus buried um with ham. Allus kept a ham a purpose slung on the bacon rack and chines, salted, hung up there in case there was a christening. And drink! They drank the dead into the ground them days, it was thought a respectable thing to do.'

As the two o'clock June sun bore down, wilting the new-mown hay, Harry's two horses plodded to the stable door, traces swinging, left, right, as they walked, the brass tips of Violet's hames, gleaming in the sun-drenched yard, touching the lintel as she passed through the door up the worn steps to her standing.

'Now old gurl,' Harry talked in the cool of the stone-flagged stable, 'let's have them gears off for an hour.' He performed his age-long custom: unreining the bridle, unchaining the hames, then with right arm under the back-band holding the right hame, left hand to left hame, lifting the light GO harness off her back onto the wooden peg sticking out of the stable wall.

'Yum sweating smartish, don't want ya sore, don't want ye pinched, whur's the brush?' First off with the bridle, undo the chin-straps, slip her ears through the headpiece and over she comes, the bit being last to leave her, she chobbles at it as if in relief. Harry pulled her collar forward, forward until she bent her neck. She knew what was happening. Finally Harry turned the collar upside down on her neck and with drooping head, she shed it in the manger. A tidemark of drying sweat marked the place where the collar fitted her shoulders. A white mark on her back showed where the back-band took the weight of the traces, and when Turpin had been undressed of his gears, Harry brushed, brushed, puffed, brushed, puffed, until their coats shone. Then, as they munched their hay in the stable shade, Harry sat and ate his late lunch, drank his sun-warmed cider, dangled his legs on the stable bench among the leather, the chains, the coupling sticks, the halters, the smell of ammonia. He sat until Mr Dunn arrived with George, and wasp-stung Tat and Blackbird.

'Well Harry, as soon as you're ready, take two horses and a wagon down to the wallies in the Dewrest. Tat's raked it, you help him pitch. George, you load the wagons. The hay's in fine fettle,' and winking at George, Mr Dunn continued, 'Tat ull tell you where there's a wasps' nest.'

'Gaffer,' Tat looked through his one eye, 'that bit of herbage anant the nest better stop till dark when them warm-assed uns be abed. They be angry since I combed um with the oss rake. They be out to drive their poisonous needles into some crater.'

The harness jingled, the wheels creaked as the men went towards the Dewrest riding the horses, loose reined with the traces acting as stirrups. They pulled the wagons, the plough lines on the filler; it was a rough passage, a springless, jolting, bone-shaking ride, nothing but long pitching shuppicks, ropes coiled and swinging from the wagon breach. Dunn's sandwiches, bottles of cider and jars of tea peeped out, hung cloakroom-like on the brass hames, shaken and jolted. In the field Jim, the son of Lofty, was waiting, twelve years old, a truant from school who had run away from home too.

'Oi, what dust thee want, Jim?' Harry called. 'Why bisn' at school?'

'I'm frightened of our Dad. I broke a tay cup, Master Penny's.'

'How the hell dids't do that?' George asked him. 'What wast thou a doing in there?'

Jim, who had killed more rabbits with catty and stone or with stone alone, was a marksman, but this was not his day.

'A quice' he said 'was a sat in our damson tree as big as a pullet. I throwed left-handed at him as he sat there cooing "My toe bleeds Betty" of a dinner time. The pebble just missed him. Master Penny's winda was open to let in the fresh air. Master Penny had bin strawberry picking.'

'Get on, Jim, we ant got all day,' Tat muttered. 'I bin stung.'

Jim finished his true but unbelievable story. 'The pebble knocked a cup o' tay out of Master Penny's hand as he was at the dinner table. Broke it, and our Dad's after me.'

'Get holt of the foremost hoss, lead him up between the wallies,' Harry said. 'We wants this hay on a wagon.'

George stood awaiting the first pitch-fulls, then they all laughed. 'I allus thought the missus used the blue bag for the whites, her as painted thee as blue as a Tory Tat.'

Tat, with one eye blue and a blue face, looked for all the world like a clown at the circus but still felt the sharp stings of the wasps.

Four fields away Milko hooked Blossom to his one-horse mower, and chattered round Halfpenny Horn. It slew the moon daisies, and meadow sweet in the hayfield of his four-cow dairy. He sat on the iron seat of his 30-inch machine, with a long ashed Woodbine hanging from his lips. His blond saxon head, hatless in the sun, matched the falling buttercups as they lay helpless behind the blade.

When the sun shone at its hottest, when the flies were angry, the bloodsuckers thirsty, was Milko's mowing time. 'Hear that,' the village said. 'Milko's a mowing, ought to bin thur at first light when the dew lay like diamonds in the rising sun.'

'Come on now, we wants an acre down this afternoon, then another tomorrow, out of the four acre, level field that floods in winter.'

The knife chattered more as the pollen fell dry on the short stubbled hay. The angry, broody partridge challenged Blossom as she left her nest of chicks. Milko dismounted and put a withy by the nest, circled it widely, leaving a little island of uncut grass for the mother and her brood. Milko cut an acre then rode his machine under the withies, sitting there to eat his tea, then he pulled a cock of green hay under Blossom's nose. Blossom, free from the flies, pulled a constant rope of green grass from the cock, chewing while Milko chewed, swigged, chewed, mopped his brow with his belted handkerchief, waited and watched the hen partridge return to her nest, then heard the busy Dunn's team hauling hay. His cows stood knee-deep in the pond under the withies, switching their tails, chewing, and their udders filling for the Midnight Milkman.

Mrs Steward's house-cum-laundry was busy. The clothes-line was empty, high from the plum to the apple tree, the pear to the cherry tree, while the kitchen table was stacked with ironed linen garments, sheets, pillow cases, bolster cases, smalls, unmentionables.

Mrs Steward's face, red as a tomato from the fire and flat iron, dripped drops of sweat on the flags of her kitchen floor as she supped a mug of tea from the hobbed teapot. She tempered her hot silver shining irons, holding them to her face, spitting on them, then trying them on an old vest to check the heat, then gliding to and fro, up and down the table. Creases vanished, sheets were smoothed, shirts looked shop-new. It was a hot ironing afternoon as sun-bleached, sun-dried linen filled the wicker clothes baskets – the Doctor's basket, Tiddley's basket, Mrs Pride's basket.

Finally, the last crease was pressed, the last sheet folded. 'It's all over. Thank God.'

Up at Coney Burrows, Flora was getting the tea for her lodger, tea for Amy and tea for her sister Lil. The oily marge on Careful Billy's anaemic batch cake bread would be helped down by a few of Lofty's strawberries. On Sunday afternoon Sacco had picked some of Lofty's strawberries, now cool in the pantry, stalked and red, ready for Ganger Firth coming hungry off the Midland Railway. He would still smell of creosote but he was Flora's pleasure, Flora's treasure. Amy's excuse to flirt with Sacco was, 'Our Mother can't say nothing. I know she's a widow, but treats him as a husband she do.' Lucky Flora, lucky Ganger.

Stodge left his barrow in the Plough and Harrow rick-yard, upside down in case of a downpour. He limped to the cottage where he had the first cup out of his wife's teapot, then moulded his taters up, tied up his beans, fed his Sunday-poaching ferret, put on his slippers, read the *Echo*, then nodded off to sleep on the sofa.

Cyril, his tea over, ambled through the village, and inspected Sacco's mound over Mrs Tomkins.

Dunn's wagons creaked as one by one the roped loads were pulled homewards to rest level in the rick-yard as Monday's sun lost its midday power and sank to sleep behind the hills. Harry talked his team through gateways. Jim, the young twelve-year-old marksman, had returned to his dad's cottage where the belt hung under the ingle, and took his leather medicine. He went supperless to bed, while Mrs Penny had her supper. Across the garden a bare hook on her dresser marked the spot where the broken crock had hung.

NO PEA-PICKERS, NO GIPSIES, the age-old sign read outside the Plough and Harrow as Romany Loveridge sweated through the taproom door.

'Nice to see you, Boy,' Frank Bird, landlord, greeted him.

'The notice still stands, Frank, but I know tis meant for the Diddies, the trouble-makers. A pint for me, one for Sacco, another for Master Pumphrey and good may it do you.'

Daylight faded as Harry and George ungeared Dunn's four horses, tired from the hayfield. They groped in the dim stable and instinctively hung up the leather and chain harness. The team snorted one by one to the water trough. Their thirst quenched, they followed Harry down the road in the evening cool to the horse field. Harry leaned for a minute on the gate after, one by one, the rope halters had slipped over their ears, and they were free. They rolled in the grass, now wet with dew. They whinnied a 'thank you' to Harry who joined George and Tat at the Plough and Harrow.

'Jesu Joy of Man's Desiring' Sacco vamped on the pub piano. Loveridge sang, the three haymakers downed their cool quarts like desert-dry Foreign Legionnaires. The pea-picking Diddies joined in from the iron-tabled garden. 'Not bad people, but not Romanies,' Loveridge told Mrs Bird.

Through the door, powdered, rouged and gallus, her hips waggling like her mother's, came Amy. 'Shandy for Amy,' called Sacco. Then calling her to the piano he said, 'Not tonight, Josephine, I'm on the ivory. Sing for the company. Sing "Ramona"'.

Amy sang while Sacco's fingers struck the piano keys. A row of pewter tankards of beer stood on the piano. As the company centred round Sacco, Frank Bird fried sausages for him which he swilled down with cold beer pumped from the cold cellar which was deeper than where Mrs Tomkins lay.

'Tidy job you made in the cemetery, Sacco,' Cyril said over his Guinness.

'Secrets I have,' Sacco said, 'that I only divulge when there's sufficient beer.'

'A quart for Sacco,' Cyril called. 'He's had a hard day among the clay.'

'Dust we are and dust returned,' he replied. 'Potent at sixty-one, Cyril. How about you and Milly?'

'That's enough,' the avowed bachelor churchwarden warned.

'What's the secret, Sacco?'

'I've earned fifteen bob today. I've buried one and throwed out two. That ground bin used afore. I got coffin plates galore in the saddle room. Pity we can't let um rest.'

Harry, Tat and George sang 'The Farmer's Boy' to Sacco's accompaniment, bringing the haymaking spirit to the village pub, but Sacco was getting under the weather fast. The harness room was four hundred yards away so once more his fingers glided over the ivories with 'Jesu Joy of Man's Desiring'.

Down at the dairy Milko enticed his four Rubies with a bucket of cake to their standings in the chill June moonlit night. As they scrubbed the wooden manger with their tongues so they gave down the midnight milk. Then, released to the grazings, the Rubies disappeared in the moonbeams and the moon daisies, while Milko's lantern-hung float started its round. Blossom pulled the float, jolting, stopping, starting, making the churns clank, a noisy midnight with its noisy buckets and noisy Milko. Night-gowned ladies and night-spirited men opened the sashes of their sleeping bedrooms shouting, 'A quart Milko', 'A pint Milko and quiet, you'll wake the village'. For ages now this had gone on. People set their clocks by him – 11.50 at Flora's, 11.55 at Ada's, and so on. He sang harvest hymns as he went. What harvest one never knew, but as he clanked his bucket to and fro Blossom knew where his next stop was as Milko's deep bass sang 'We plough the fields and scatter' on a stage devoid of birdsong other than the hoot of owls. 'I'm a native,' Milko would say. 'Our family goes back to Queen Elizabeth, we're the oldest family in The Cuckoo Pen. The seed time and the harvest . . .'

'Four pints,' shouted Revd Vernon, night-shirted at his study door. 'We have visitors tomorrow.'

'Is this the morning or afternoon milk?' Cyril Pumphrey queried over the pint of milk after several pints of stout.

Milko served the village faithfully in all weathers. 'All good gifts around us are sent from Heaven above . . .'

'Heavens above, Milko, unt there no rest?' Lofty who had been strawberry picking, reeled from his warm bed to the window; he was whacked that midnight.

Milly Bostock lay cool in her lavender-scented bed in the open-windowed bedroom where, before she blew out the candle, the bob howlers, the night moths, circled the light. She dreamed of men in uniform, always men in uniform. She relived the night when Tom Solway, Captain of the Fire Brigade, carried her, nightdressed, in his arms under the sashes, down the ladder, as smoke from her fired chimney billowed in the bedroom. His brassed helmet, his belted axe, his waxed moustache, were as vivid as that winter night when she lay in his arms. He had taken her to the lych-gate and as the cool air revived her breathing and her eyes opened he pressed his waxed moustache against her virgin lips. The fire still smouldered in her June dreamland. She dreamed of Sergeant Jones warning her of the Zeppelin raids as he entered her unlocked back door, stood uniformed, dazzling silver, at the foot of her stairs and three yards away in silken nightie she chattered for half an hour. His deep warming voice had made it worth all the Kaiser's Zeppelins crossing The Cuckoo Pen.

Amy at Coney Burrows giggled under the sheets thinking of Sacco, then she frowned, dreading tomorrow when she would be charring, scrubbing, dusting, slop-pail emptying, lamp trimming, candlestick scraping, potato scraping, doing the rounds of the homes of the chosen few of The Cuckoo Pen.

Ganger Firth drowsed on Flora's duck down bed, floating on breast feathers, listening to the Midland goods as she laboured up Sanfield Hill, hearing the noisy clank of wheels on the old road, then laying back with pride as she quietly glided down hill where his relay gang took the clatter from the night air. It was a peaceful night at Coney Burrows.

As uncorsetted Mrs Pride lay between the brass golden gates of the four foot six bed, her bosom formed two velvet hills with a valley between. Here Monkey Brand layed his copper-bristled chin. He ebbed and flowed as the hills rose and fell both sides of the valley. He dreamed of blacklead, heard church bells, half aware smelled the lavender-scented nightgown. Tartly his wife muttered 'Teddy' and he, pretending sleep, snuggled deeper into the haven, but not for long as she turned her twice Teddy-sized frame throwing him, broncho-like, to the bed edge.

'Four loads of wilted herbage, sweet as honey,' Farmer Dunn announced from his wing-back chair as he and his wife stayed up into the summer night, a night when the open door let in the cool mist which mounted the staircase, and cleared the bedrooms of hot air, throwing it through the open casements. But Farmer Dunn thought, 'I must have a last look round. The men are resting. I must look at the loads.'

Lantern in hand he toured the rick-yard, pulled the wisps of hay from the roped, loaded wagons, smelt it as he walked, chewed the sweet grains, rubbed the clover, blew it like tobacco in his cupped hands. 'The cows will relish this when there's hoar-frost on the hedges and snow driven in the lane.'

Ada mooed, bawling for her calf. The poplars screamed as they rubbed each other in the breeze of the spinney. A rat ran thirsty to the stream. Frogs croaked in the horse pond. Dunn's men were sleeping. Even Sacco was sleeping. But nature was at work. Hedgehogs crossed the Dirty Lane, cats fought on the barn roofs, moles heaved the soil, sheep grazed in the cool night, cows mooed in the lush green field, free from the flies and the glare of the sun.

For the first time in years Farmer Dunn lit his pipe in the still rick-yard. If only George and Harry knew, they had warned often enough! But the fallen hay from the wagon was dew drenched, the grass soaking, so different from mid-summer day's sun, and there was no danger of fire.

Returning to the farmhouse Mrs Dunn lay asleep in her chair, so, slippered, Farmer Dunn took a jug down the cellar steps and drew a quart of Malvern Hill Perry. He carried it up to his wife and they drank the ice cool champagne of the Mid-West as the clock struck midnight. 'Up the wooden hill, Missus, we be both tired. Take your candle. I'll be along.'

On the Farm

FARMER DUNN AND HIS MEN

On a June morning the heavy dew drenched the swathes of hay in Carrants Field meadow. Four wagon loads of hay stood in Dunn's rick-yard waiting to be unloaded on to the rick; yellow painted wagons with the owners' name in red at the end, names forgotten of farmers long since dead, a part of Dunn's collection from farm sales.

At 7 o'clock George, with battered trilby and in shirt sleeves, emerged from the cowshed covered in hay seeds, hedgehog-like.

'Where's Harry and Caleb, Gaffer? We want these wagons unloaded by bait time, and when the sun gets up Carrants Field will be ready to carry.'

Farmer Dunn looked across the yard. 'Here they are, George, both of them. You and Harry come up on the rick and Caleb can unload the wagons.'

Silently the men worked as Farmer Dunn built the rick.

'I got a problem with Flora my housekeeper, Gaffer. Her do ask for money every day. Tis monotonous. Her do want money now to buy a new hat for Lill's wedding. That's if ever her do marry Sacco.'

George said, 'Tis like that with some women. Thee bist entangled with a cunning widow, Caleb. Two of the strongest things there are in this world are gunpowder and women. Gunpowder will blow you up and women will draw ya.'

Dunn's wagons were unloaded by bait time. George and Farmer Dunn rode in the broad-wheeled one down to Carrants Field, Harry

with Diamond in the shafts led the way down Gipsies Lane. W.D.
JORDAN, BROAD MARSTON GROUNDS the writing on the wagon
said, and one wondered who was Mr Jordan?

The hay, some in swathes, some in wind-rows, had dried in the
sun. George and Harry pitched with their long forks, or shuppicks,
to Farmer Dunn on the load.

After he had eaten his dinner, Caleb was to shoe a couple of horses
for neighbours in Dunn's smithy.

CALEB AND FLORA

Up in Coney Burrows Flora prepared the meal. A plain meal but
good. 'Come, my love, dinner's ready.'

Her call from the hill to where her man plodded up the footpath
made Caleb think. 'Does her want money for the train fare to town?
Just let her ask me again!'

Surprises are quite usual at Coney Burrows. Dinner over, Caleb
made his way to the wicket gate where the footpath from the
cottage led to the village and Farmer Dunn's smithy.

'You never kissed me, Caleb.'

He turned and gave Flora a bristly kiss. Flora had to pluck up
courage then. 'Give me my train fare to town, Dear. I've got half a
crown for a new hat.'

The blacksmith gave no answer but hurried down the path.

In a field by the Chapel a neighbour kept a few cows. To prevent
abortion the old idea was to graze a donkey with the herd. They
would eat the poisonous plants which harmed the cows.

'Yer, Neddy. I wants thee this afternoon.'

Taking off his broad leather belt Caleb slung it around the
donkey's neck leading him to Coney Burrows.

Lill, back from her morning job cleaning, dusting and washing
for Mildred at Apple Acre, sat reading a novel in a chair on the little
lawn in front of Coney Burrows.

'Mum,' she called, 'Caleb's back here with a donkey.'

'Out of the way. You and your mother.' The blacksmith spoke sharply and led the donkey through the front door into Flora's kitchen. 'Now, Flora. Let me give you a leg up and you can ride in style to the town.'

'You shouldn't do that, Caleb, to our Mother. You'll make her have one of her turns.' Lill was angry but then Flora saw the funny side and decided that she would not be shopping in town that day.

Joe and Lofty, sweating among the strawberries, were sitting under their damson trees eating bread, fat bacon, and onions. It was dinner time at Hales Acre.

Joe said, 'It's a prayer meeting tonight, brother, at Chapel.'

'I bin thinking. The Poor Box, I emptied it last week and gave sixteen shillings to Flora,' Lofty said. 'Now she is living along with Caleb. I'll pray for them tonight. Tis not according to The Word. First her lived with Ganger Firth, now tis Caleb.'

THE MIDNIGHT MILKMAN

The sun went down behind The Cuckoo Pen, that circle of beech trees high on the hill above Coney Burrows. An ancient enclosure, the ancestors of the village would try in vain to pen in the cuckoo there so that the village could have perpetual summer. Tomorrow the cuckoo would return to the land in the south. He always left the village on the day of the horse fair.

Milko, the Midnight Milkman, was having his evening meal before leaving his ancestral home where for 500 years the land had been farmed by his forebears. Since the death of their parents Milko and his brother, both bachelors, had led Bohemian lives. Still with a steady income from land and investments, the two young men played at farming.

Milko, the elder brother, had let himself go, rising at midday, milking his cows, sleeping the afternoon away, then milking at midnight. His lifestyle, so alien to the village farmers, may have been to just show the world that he, Milko, was independent, from a family who had farmed there for 500 years, and the Lord of the Manor.

Milko had fine clothes hung in huge wardrobes beside his four-poster bed. These he wore on his fortnightly trips to Cheltenham in his Britain car with Sacco. There the pair of village misfits wined and dined with the tarts of Lower Dockham.

At the farm and at Pecked Medda where his little herd of red Rubies (Devon) cows provided milk for some of the village, Milko was a different character. A blond mop of hair partly covered with a greasy trilby, a bristly chin, a perpetual grin and the eternal Woodbine cigarette all gave him a vagrant look. His woollen jersey of yellow peeped out above his coat made of goatskin. He had made the coat himself, slaughtering the animal then curing the skin to make a two coloured jacket. His breeches were stiff with the muck from the cowshed; gaiters and hobnailed boots completed the picture.

Milko kept his cows at Pecked Medda, half a mile from his home, between the branch railway and the main road. With his horse Dick, a half-bred hunter which he rode at times but which normally pulled his float, Milko would travel his usual route along the cart track from The Chestnuts, an ancient track past badger earths at Land Close. Twice in twenty-four hours this blond dairy man stood amidships on his float, like a galleon passing between the hawthorn hedges on a summer's day. He would survey his fields as the float bounced its way past his mangol wurzels, his uncut mowing grass, and his late brussels sprouts. Everything was late on Milko's farm. Rising as he did at midday he never caught up.

The hurricane lantern swung on the overhead beam and Milko spoke kindly to his red Rubies. The shadows flickered as he milked one, two, three, four, five, and hoisted the churn into his float. His half-hunter watch said midnight.

Dick, the nag, turned for home over the railway crossing and up the cart track.

'Dick, you wasted life, think I stole ya. Come on, boy, we are late.'

The moon that night peeped over the Cotswold edge and the tawny owl hooted from the spinney, 'Ta wit, ta wit, ta wo'.

Milko, who studied the weather, thought, 'A fine day tomorrow. Perhaps I'll mow the meadow with Dick in the shafts.'

At The Chestnuts Dick was tethered to the gatepost. Milko drained part of the milk from the churns into a bucket with a pint measure hung on the side. This was where his deliveries began.

'All is safely gathered in, ere the winter storms begin,' his clarion voice rang through the village street. Men and their wives lit candles, and looked at the time.

'Half past twelve! Oh, my God! I thought it was time to get up,' Harry, the carter, muttered to his wife.

Dogs started barking, children cried and Milko continued with his Harvest hymns. 'We plough the fields and scatter the good seed on the land. Where's Mrs Penny's jug?' In the lantern light Milko poured out the measure for the retired gardener and his wife.

'Milko, Milko!' Mr Penny called at the bedroom window.

The blond Midnight Milkman continued to sing. 'All is safely gathered in. What is it Mr Penny?'

'Milko, I say is that the morning milk or the evening?'

'All the milk from my red Rubies is good, Sir. Milk from these Devon cows isn't like that from the other dairy — watery Friesian milk. Good night to you Mr Penny.'

Mr Penny slammed the window, saying, 'Good night! We've been in bed for three hours.'

When all his customers had been served Milko had several pints over. 'This will be sour by tomorrow and it will do me as much good as anybody,' the Midnight Milkman said to Sacco, who was up at dawn that day at the door of the harness room where he lived at Dunn's Farm. 'Let's share it, Brother.'

He filled Sacco's jug, a present to the mason. Then he tipped the bucket to his lips, and drank the last of the lactic fluid from the Rubies. Stabling Dick at The Chestnuts Milko climbed the stairs as the birds started to sing in the orchard. He slept till midday. All was safely gathered in.

THE COLONEL

From The Cuckoo Pen, past Coney Burrows and Flora's cottage, past the big wood, a mass of bluebells in the spring and rhododendrons in summer, and on beyond that the Colonel farmed the eastern slopes of the hill. Grey haired and grey moustached, he rode a grey hunter. He was as upright as a skittle, lean and fit at seventy-five. The Colonel, I suppose, was one of the personalities of farming. He served in the First World War as an officer; ordering the ranks came naturally to him.

Some say the tied cottage was a good thing but the Colonel used his as a means to bargain. 'If you are not on the hayfield by 10 o'clock on Sunday morning you are sacked and out of my cottage.' These words threatened many a young man, even those with small children. Yet there were so many sides to the Colonel. He was fond of children, giving parties at Christmas for the village boys and girls.

I knew him as a prominent member of the Farmers' Union who, at one meeting, brought the house down with a slip of the tongue. The subject under discussion was that of bulls straying on to neighbour's land and serving young heifers before they were fully grown. The Colonel, on his feet near me at the meeting, declared that if you have heifers in one field and a bull in the adjoining field and one of the heifers is bulling it is only 'human' nature for the bull to break the fence and serve the heifer.

Hunting was the Colonel's favourite pastime and the baying of hounds as Reynard ran from the beech covers was music to him. To call those fox hounds 'dogs' was red rag to a bull with the Colonel.

As a farmer I did on the whole have good neighbours and I tried to be the same. I wouldn't say that the Colonel was wholly a bad neighbour but we lived on different plains. It was a Saturday afternoon when I found the Colonel's Jack Russell among my lambing ewes. Putting the dog in my Land Rover, I took him home and housed him in the stable then rang the Colonel.

'I've had a hard day hunting, man,' he said. 'I'm about to have a bath. I'll come down after tea. Why didn't you kick him in the ass and send him home?'

There was really no answer to that, but the Colonel did come later to collect his dog.

The village policeman said to me, 'Why didn't you summons the Colonel, for if the dog is among sheep it's technically worrying the sheep.'

'Come off it!' I replied. 'The Colonel is Chairman of the Local Magistrates.'

Then three of my ewes strayed on to the Colonel's land. The phone wires were pretty hot as he explained, 'I'm keeping everybody's ewes. Yours and Fowlers. Come and fetch yours, they are in the pen at the farm.'

Sacco and I took the Land Rover to the farm, collected the sheep and took them straight to market. These were the wanderers and I had no more trouble with the flock after that.

The last brush I had with the Colonel involved one of his hunters. My cattle were in a field known as Big Holbrook, adjoining the Colonel's farm. One night one of his hunters broke the fence, chasing my cattle through a barbed wire fence. They were petrified. The Colonel's hunter was what is known as a rig or a rudgel, a half-cut stallion, animals which can be gentlemen one day and devils the next.

We collected the cattle next morning and put them back in the field, then mended the fence and rang the Colonel.

'Damn it! We are busy with the hay but I'll fetch the horse on Sunday.'

'That's no good,' I replied. 'He's chasing my cattle again.'

I rang the police and the Colonel was very cross and a horse-dealer friend of mine advised me not to go in the field with the rudgel.

GRIPES, FLUKE AND
FOOT AND MOUTH

In the 1920s animal diseases which can be cured or prevented today were rife. Turpin, Harry's foremost horse in the plough team, had a nasty habit of breaking the fence into the home orchard and filling his belly with apples. Gripes, when the horse is blown with gases, is a harmful condition. In fact the animal can be in such a state as to attack the horseman open mouthed.

The old remedy of linseed oil and turpentine usually worked, and the other important thing was to keep the horse walking. I can picture Harry now as he endeavoured to walk Turpin up and down the farmyard on a halter. If loosed for a moment the horse would lie down and groan in pain.

It's a fact that a horse's stomach, unlike humans, has continual collywobbles. It's when it stops rumbling that there's trouble. Every time Harry came back down the yard to the stable door he stopped with his ear against Turpin's ribs and listened. We dare not speak or make a noise. Harry was listening for rumbling. When the medicine worked and Turpin attempted to what Harry called stale he was relieved, whistling to his charge, and he turned to me with the words, 'Now he's pissed he'll be alright.'

What I have learnt about farm animals is how cows can withstand difficult calving and other problems, while horses and sheep would succumb.

Liver fluke in sheep used to be a killer. Like tuberculosis in humans there was no cure in the 1920s. Neither was' there prevention by vaccination for pulpy kidney disease in lambs and the scourge of lamb dysentery. Liver fluke wiped out thousands in the wet year 1879, and recurred again in the 1920s. The disease is caused by a little snail and is a problem in the Vale rather than the hill land. The old shepherd used to recognize the sheep which were affected because they had glassy eyes and lumpy jaws. When Dunn's ewes started dying the shepherd took it as a reflection on his shepherding, coming to Dunn's door on pay night offering to pack up his job as shepherd and commit suicide.

'What are you threatening to do, Shepherd?' Tom Dunn asked him with a worried look.

'I'd a good mind to jump in the moat pond, Master, and end it all. There's one tool I don't like carrying as a shepherd, it's this here spade. I buried four this morning.'

The shepherd didn't jump into the moat pond and the following year a treatment for liver fluke did save the lives of many sheep.

The old shepherd still declared that when a young lamb died suddenly and frothed at the mouth the reason was some wool in the maw. Lambs do have a tendency to pick bits of wool hanging from the wooden sheep troughs. The old idea was that the wool with the ewes' milk formed a blockage in the gullet. It's since been proved that the lambs died from pulpy kidney disease which is now prevented by either a vaccine or a serum.

In the early 1920s Tom Dunn's animals did suffer and die from disease. His milking herd was not free from tragedy. Blenheim found one of the best cows in the herd dead down by Carrants Brook in a field known as Didcot Ham. Tom Dunn sent a telegram to the knacker man to fetch the carcase.

'Not before I've skinned her, Master. I can make five bob of the skin.'

Blenheim was quite deft with a sharp knife. He had almost finished skinning the cow when Mr Hodworth, the vet arrived. Tom Dunn had sent Tustin on his bike for the vet. 'Stop, Stop man! Throw away the knife. We have a case of Anthrax here, one little cut on your hand and you would be dead.'

That's why shaving brushes are made from badger hair. Badgers don't get Anthrax.

The carcase was then burned.

Whether or not it was the shock of the case of Anthrax, Blenheim took what he called his Lloyd George pension, retiring to his cottage at Bachelor's Avenue.

The same week Whistler, the drunken nephew of Maxim and Tart, died. Since his army career in the RAVC he had been a very good blacksmith, until drink became his downfall.

Stocky and Sacco dug the grave and Sacco as usual helped to carry the old soldier. Maxim and Tart did attend, remarking what a lot of dead folks there were in the churchyard. There was no love lost between these two old 'Contrary Sods', as Blenheim described them, and Whistler.

It was said at the grave side, 'What a lovely lot of flowers from his friends.'

Maxim in his usual clumsy vein replied, 'Ah, that's as maybe, a lot of flowers. I happen to know that Whistler had no time for flowers and if they had put a sack of taters on top of him Whistler would have been just as happy.'

As Blenheim had retired Tom Dunn was looking for a cowman to replace him. Fred Hawker was chosen. He had recently moved from a cottage in Bachelor's Avenue to a little thatched cot near Dunn's farmyard. His four daughters had all grown up; one had married Sacco.

Tom Dunn now had a herd of twenty-five Shorthorn cows and Fred was sending the milk away by train from the station to Birmingham in seventeen-gallon churns. Fred was a quiet, thoughtful man who got on well with the other workers.

Young Jim, the under cowman, was mischievous, teasing, typical of a sixteen-year-old youth. Fred worried about his cows even more than his employer. When he was short of churns to put the milk in he would wring his hands saying to young Jim, 'Whatever be us going to do with the milk?'

Jim smiled and uttered this suggestion, 'Well Fred, we shall have to dig a hole and put it in.'

Which brought the reply, 'Don't thee talk so stupid among all this work.'

Whereas Blenheim had been a customer of Frank Bird at the Plough and Harrow ever since he could lift a pint of cider, Fred was an abstainer and strong Chapel. I was fond of Fred Hawker. He

A farmer of The Cuckoo Pen and Chairman of the Parish Council

The Plough and Harrow pub, where the labourers of The Cuckoo Pen took their refreshment

The Cuckoo Pen, Bredon Hill, as it is today, a shadow of its former self

Tom Dunn's carter with Boxer, his favourite plough horse

Haymaking with scythe and horse rake

The fast motor bike. It attracted the girls of The Cuckoo Pen

Strawberry-pickers early on a Monday morning, June 1911

Pea-pickers with sun bonnets and straw hats

Coney Burrows. Flora's home on the hill

The hay rick, a family affair with the elevator

Mowing the hay with two horses in double harness

Plum-pickers. Tom Dunn's gang in the orchard

Ready for Church. Only the best clothes would do for Sunday

treated me like a son, taught me to milk a cow, to lead a calf on a halter, and like many men of his day, he was a good shot with a catapult. I learnt the names of the birds and the names he gave them. He talked of titty obbins for robins and when I was teasing him he would say, 'You sounds as if you had found a titty obbins nest and were laughing at the balchins [the bald chicks].'

I have happy memories of Fred – oh, but I called him 'Mr Hawker'. We had to respect our elders. When the cows had been milked Fred would cool gallons of it by pouring the buckets into a tank and then it ran over a corrugated stainless steel affair down into a churn. I thought it was magic.

The whole thing took time and as the cows on winter nights pulled at the hay from their racks and ate their bait of chaff, mangolds, ground oats and cattle cake, Fred Hawker played his tin whistle. As a small boy I sat beside this guru and listened to the tunes he played. Many were Sankey and Moody hymns but Fred did play folk songs too. In those pre-wireless days when we were starved of music apart from Chapel hymns and a few scratchy pieces on the phonograph, Fred's tin whistle made those winter evenings so much brighter. Sometimes he sang to me 'Dare to be a Daniel, dare to stand alone'. The lessons in Fred's dairy gave more sense to life than those at school.

An aged Hereford cow named Granny, the mother of Joker the bull, stood in what Fred called the Lidded Place, a stable-like building with a stable door. She shared the stalls with Peasgood, a strawberry roan. Fred often milked these two cows last, and reminded me that he called Granny 'The babby's cow'. You see, many babies, myself included, were fussy of what milk they were fed on. In the years at the beginning of the First World War it's doubtful if the word 'allergic' had been coined. I was reared on Granny the Hereford cow's milk. Blenheim told Fred how he took the milk from Granny to Mother every morning and night. I don't know how old the Hereford cow was when I sat with Fred in the dairy. One thing that Fred knew though was how hard this cow called Granny was to milk.

'No good you trying to milk her my boy,' he said. 'Your little hand won't be big enough to hold her tits.' Her tits were enormous.

Fred's pride and joy was a cow named Spot. She was a sandy brown with a spot between her horns. She gave over five gallons of milk a day, quite something in 1923.

On 11 November 1923 Fred Hawker brought his herd of Shorthorn cows up Gipsies Lane to Tom Dunn's farm for evening milking. He noticed some of the animals were lame but the lane was rough and lame cows had been a problem before. Because of the wet brookside meadows of Didcot Ham cows did develop a condition Fred called low, or foul in the foot. This could be cured by hot bran poulticing. But for several cows to be lame worried Fred.

When the cows were chained up in the long shed Fred fetched Tom Dunn.

'Master,' he said, 'some of the cows be lame and two be dribbling at the mouth.'

Tom Dunn, a good judge of animal conditions, knew this to be foot and mouth disease. It so happened that Tom Dunn had just been connected to the telephone and this proved a great help as his farm was very isolated from the outside world. He rang the vet, who came and confirmed foot and mouth and reported the outbreak to the Ministry of Agriculture.

The next day the Ministry vets arrived and the police made Tom Dunn's farm a 'no-go' area, with buckets of Jeyes fluid at the entrance gates where the postman dipped his boots. The cows were kept in and the affected ones were unable to eat. A valuer came to put a price on the animals, which were looking quite out of condition.

The following day the slaughter man came with his humane killer and Harry brought a dray load of coal from the station. Young Jim, the under cowman, collected a cart load of wood. The cows were to be burned in Tom Dunn's half-acre garden.

Men were busy digging a trench around the proposed fire to act as a drain from the animals. The oil man from town delivered a forty-gallon barrel of paraffin to drench the carcases when they were on the funeral pyre. Harry decided that Turpin, that powerful cart horse in traces, was to drag the carcases on to the fire. The scene that foggy November day was one of sadness.

'Where's Fred Hawker?' Harry asked young Jim.

'Oh, he's in the barn sat on a truss of hay away from it all.' When the first report of the humane killer rang across the yard Fred ran to Tom Dunn's back door with tears streaming down his face. 'I can't stop here Master, and watch this lot. Can I go home?'

Tom Dunn, almost in tears himself replied, 'You go home Fred. We'll manage.'

I didn't go to school that day. Our privy was up the garden among the nut bushes. I sat there and watched through a little window. The calendar on the wall had a picture of a shepherd carrying a lamb across his shoulders in a snowstorm. Underneath were the words of Cardinal Newman's famous hymn 'Lead kindly light amid the encircling gloom'. An eight-year-old boy sitting there didn't quite understand the gloom in Fred Hawker's heart but the whole meaning of life with his cows had been darkened.

As the cows were shot one by one and dragged to the fire by Turpin, the next one for execution seemed to know; they smelt death, but the job had to be done. The firewood, coal and paraffin blazed, and the smell of the burnt flesh wafted over The Cuckoo Pen. The village mourned for Tom Dunn and Fred Hawker. Ten weaned calves were slaughtered but they were not infected and went to the butchers in the town.

I was excited that PC Smith, our local constable, stopped all night in the farmhouse. He had to see that the letter of the law was observed. Men stayed by the fire through the night. When morning came Tom Dunn produced some calves' liver for breakfast, something I heartily enjoyed sitting at the table beside uniformed PC Smith.

That evening I was sent with a milk can to fetch milk from Mr Clements' dairy. He came to the door and invited me in, then filled my milk can.

'How much does Mr Dunn owe you, Mr Clements?'

'Oh, my boy, I'm so sorry to hear of the loss of his cows. I went to school with Tom, we have been great friends. That drop of milk he is welcome to. Give him my regards.'

As I came down the road from the dairy the flames from the fire reflected in the night sky and the silhouette of two men watching looked eerie.

Several dry cows escaped the slaughter, they were a mile away in Long Dewrest. Among them was old Granny the babby's cow. The Ministry vets threatened Joker the bull, Granny's calf, but he was tied up at the bull pen a distance from the long shed and had a reprieve.

Blenheim came down with Laughing Tom with stories of foot and mouth in the Squires Lane. Laughing Tom described how when the Squire's cows had the disease they were not slaughtered but fed with sloppy bran mash to keep them alive. Blenheim chimed in, 'Ah, but they got devilishly poor, I know they lived but they was as thin as hurdles.'

It took some days for the carcases of seventeen cows to turn to ashes. A fortnight after the fire the ashes were still hot but were scattered over Tom Dunn's garden. Only a few bits of bone remained as a reminder that here in the garden seventeen beautiful Shorthorn cows had died.

Tom Dunn bought a dozen Shorthorn heifers from Ireland and again had bad luck. They aborted, what Blenheim called 'slipped their calves'. He never had another herd of cows like the ones Fred Hawker milked.

You may ask what happened to Fred Hawker. He never came back, spending his days in summer time under his apple tree playing his melodion or his tin whistle. I sat with him, and he told me the Doctor said he had heart trouble.

When Fred died it's true that it was because of heart trouble, for the cowman died of a broken heart.

The Villagers

THE MERRY WIDOW

One Monday morning Blenheim propelled himself up Gipsies Lane leaning heavily on his ash plant. The little herd of Dunn's Shorthorns had an alien beast, Mrs Dunn's pet, but Blenheim's problem. The Alderney called Brindy with a crumpled horn led the little herd astray.

'Damn you, Brindy. I'll strike thee like Moses struck the rock with the children of Israel.'

The little old cow ran under the drooping ash outside Olive's Apple Acre to ward off the flies.

Fred Tredwell from the post office on his way with the letters skimmed past Blenheim on his bike. 'Got your Papers yet, Blenheim?' this sarcastic postmaster called out.

Blenheim stood as upright as his game leg would allow, cleared his throat, shouted loudly to Tredwell so that all the village women hanging their washing out on that morning could hear. 'Papers, Papers, Tredwell! Who was it had the rheumatics and bellyache during the last war and got Dr Overthrow to get him out of the Army and then never voted for him at the election?'

Back at Apple Acre Olive approached Blenheim as he returned from driving his herd to Didcot Ham. 'I just want a word with you, Cowman. You know what happened the other night? Your bull kept me awake.'

'Oh, Mam, Joker did get out. I be sorry.'

'Yes,' Olive replied, 'and he was hung from his ring all night long. His ring was fixed on my arrowhead railings. He bawled all night long and I was entertaining Sam the paddle-steamer owner from town.'

'Entertaining you call it, Mam. Is that what it is?'

'Now, Blenheim, that's quite enough, but secure that bull.'

'Master Dunn has put a leather washer on his chain. He will never get loose again.'

Speaking kindly to the cowman, Olive said that she heard Tredwell asking him if he had his call-up papers. 'That was cruel, Blenheim, and Tredwell who got out of the army in 1914. I must go now off to Cheltenham with Polly, my cob, and the governess car. Your arthritis, Blenheim, you know I was a nurse. I'll bring some embrocation from the chemist's. Come down this evening and I'll massage your hip.'

'Thank you kindly, Mam. That's Christian of you.'

Olive's cob broke into a canter along the 1 mile straight of Poplar Row, passing the turnpike house, Cheltenham bound.

Olive's mind had time to think of the life around The Cuckoo Pen, of Flora, poor Flora, banned from the Mothers' Union for living with Caleb, the blacksmith. 'Oh the folly of it all,' Olive mulled as her governess car entered tree-lined Pitville. 'What does Miss Jeffreys know of marriage, the spinster who runs the Mothers' Union. Oh, I could tell her.'

In the yard of the Plough Olive stabled her cob and thoughts of her late husband flooded back. 'What a man was Alfred, how he spent those sovereigns left by his mother. And the honeymoon! Bournemouth was fine but Alfred's case when we went to the bedroom! Well, he had packed two Oxford shirts and a pair of hobnailed boots. What did the best man say? That Alfred expected some hard going. Not likely, he need not have worried.

'Oh, here's a really nice pair of shoes in Cavendish House. I'll try a pair. Funny my size is the same as Flora's, size 6.

'Oh Flora with that black velvet neckband, Flora whose father had a groom, you shall have my cast-off shoes. Your husband died for his country, mine through drink. We are both watched by the Holier Than Thou women of The Cuckoo Pen. The Mothers' Union would have you rid of Caleb. No, Flora, I'll stand by you,' were Olive's thoughts as she drove home.

Back towards Apple Acre the wind blew the receipted bill from the shoebox, or was it deliberate? The paper floated in the village street telling all of The Cuckoo Pen that Olive had paid £5 10s for her shoes. The roadman took it to the pub and men choked over their cider.

Olive smiled when the news came via Milko of Snob's visit to the Doctor. 'Overdoing his nature' with Olive. 'Take it easy for a while, Snob. I could prescribe Bromide but just take it easy' was the Doctor's advice.

Milko, singing his way through his milk round, broadcast to his customers that Snob had overdone his nature.

Oh Olive! What a lady, a lady and a half. Snob walked wearily to the Plough pub where old Jubilee was sitting on a bench beside Sacco and Caleb.

'How bist, Old Butt?' were Caleb's first words to Snob. The shoemaker had received his pension that morning, delivered by Conny Tredwell. 'Middling, very middling,' was the reply.

'They says that thee hast bin overdoing it along uv Olive.' These words were like putting a match to a powder magazine. 'They says tells lies,' came from Snob like a shot, a shot from an old soldier of the Grenadier Guards.

THE BOAR AND THE OLD SOLDIER

Frank Bird, landlord of the Plough, looked forward to Snob's pension day, for every month the old soldier was free with his money. Was it Revd Vernon or was it Cyril the churchwarden who persuaded Frank to have a swear box in his pub? The proceeds went to the choir outing. Snob was perhaps the best contributor to the box.

'A funny sort of illness, overdoing thy nature,' Whistler whispered to Sacco.

'It's not possible, I've proved it,' came Sacco's reply.

Snob drank deep of Fowler's Brew and ordered another straight away. He was silent, thinking, wondering who was the lucky man at Apple Acre that night. Was it that music man. 'I'll be back,' he thought. 'I'll be back.'

'Yu bient up to it along of Olive,' Blenheim remarked.

Snob took three strides across Landlord Bird's tap-room floor, shook his fist at Blenheim and called him all the words he could think of except Christian. His language was so bad that Frank Bird's swear box rattled again and again. It was half-filled by the stream of abuse to Blenheim and those who laughed with him.

Sacco, the blue-eyed, blond-haired picture of physical fitness, turned to Snob. 'Leave Olive to the men,' he taunted.

This brought another onslaught of foul language. Cyril, the churchwarden, from his corner seat said, 'Just leave Snob alone.'

'You'm a nice one to talk. You who take the choir on their outing from the swear box. A bachelor, Cyril, who is frightened of Bunch in the churchyard.'

Jarvie, the gamekeeper, quietly whispered to Snob, 'Do you really want to get back on Olive's books? Cos I got a plan. Come along a me out on to the gravel. It's a secret between thee and me.'

Snob followed the gamekeeper out on to the gravel and here the plans were laid. 'Snob, I got to kill a boar pig of Olive's. It's going to be tricky for every day I pass the sty he roars at me like a lion. You, Snob, ex-Grenadier Guards, should be pretty smart at the trigger of an army rifle. I want you to shoot the boar pig.'

Next morning after a heavy dew the signs were for a very hot day. Snob and Jarvie met at Olive's yard at 7 o'clock as planned. Jarvie was carrying an army rifle, a short piece of rope and his pig-killing gear, knives, hooks, and the like. Snob knew that Jarvie's pig killing always took place from November until March when the sides of bacon could be salted down, cured and kept for twelve months.

'What's going to happen to Olive's boar?' Snob questioned.

''Tis arranged. I'm taking the sides to the sausage factory tomorrow.'

The two men approached the sty and the old boar pig roared. Taking an apple from his pocket Jarvie cut it in pieces and rubbed the apple on the noosed rope, dangling the rope over the gate of the sty. He gave another apple to the condemned pig, then held the apple-dressed noose over the gate, a big noose to hold the boar's long tusks. Inquisitive and hungry that morning the boar licked the apple juice from the rope, venturing inch by inch until his snout and tusks were in the noose. As quick as lightning Snob pulled the rope and fastened the boar to the rail of the gate. Snob stood, soldier-like, a few feet from the gate. Jarvie stood aside. The report from Snob's rifle stirred the folk of The Cuckoo Pen. The boar fell to the floor and in went Jarvie's knife.

'Cooee, cooee!' a voice called from Olive's bedroom window, where the Merry Widow stood in her silky nightdress. She was alone.

After the two men had burnt the hair from this twenty score carcase and slung it over a beam in Olive's barn, Jarvie dressed it and found the bullet from Snob's rifle shot halfway along the boar's backbone. Olive invited the men for lunch. Jarvie left soon after, but Snob was invited to stay and he and Olive were what is known as First Cousins once again.

PONTO AND JUBILEE

Ponto, that blue-eyed, unshaven little fellow, slept rough in one of Dunn's wagons in the cart shed. Ponto was a simple, harmless mortal, the son of an insurance agent, who in his twenties was crossed on love and became one of the genuine great unwashed of no fixed abode.

The Pontos of the village early in this century found work on the farms doing boys' jobs where their feeble minds were never stretched. They fitted in, leading horses, driving the plough teams, running errands.

During the First World War, when food was rationed and could only be bought with coupons, Ponto fell foul of the authorities. A little man with a big appetite he ate all his rations in one go and then was in trouble. Kicking on the post office door and being refused more rations, Ponto called out to Fred Tredwell, Cissy's father, 'I allus had plenty of food when Master Pitman kept the shop.'

This was followed by a stream of abuse and a visit from PC Smith. Oh, it sorted itself out when Farmer Dunn supplemented Ponto's rations with some home-cured bacon, and Bunch, the organ player, amateur nurse, and a caring lady, took beef tea to the cart shed.

Everything that went wrong in Ponto's little world he blamed on the Russians. Leading the horse for Harry, Farmer Dunn's carter, high up on the hill, Ponto, who liked his pipe of tobacco, left his pipe, matches and tobacco on the Cotswold stone wall. The two men were drilling turnips and the weather in that early summer of 1921 was blistering hot. Ponto's matches ignited in the hot sun. The Russians had the blame! When shots were fired at the crows on the peas it was the Russians, and Ponto would run shouting up the village street.

Some folk were kind to this little man, but he was teased shamefully. The porter at the station took a telegram to the cart house, a spurious telegram, saying that a food parcel was due by train at the station the following day. Ponto met every train that day but no parcel arrived, which he said was promised from a distant relation, with hams of bacon and tins of beef.

This unscrupulous railwayman then told Ponto that the parcel had been left at the railway junction by mistake. This station was 7 miles away. Off went Ponto, waiting for trains on the main line, but still no parcel. This was just one of the pranks played on this harmless little old man.

Some pranks, however, can end in tragedy. Some of the lads in the village told Ponto that the Devil was hiding under some ivy covering an old gravestone in the churchyard. In fact, Whistler was there, and Ponto, intent to kill the Devil, took an axe from Frank

Bird's workshop at the Plough and with all his might cut away the ivy on the gravestone. Luckily Whistler had moved just in time. But essentially Ponto was a happy man if only he was left alone.

At Christmas his plaintive high-pitched voice could be heard singing carols around the village. 'Wild Shepherds Watch,' he sang for apples, oranges and cider. Mrs Dunn gave him some strawberry jelly, which was something entirely new to Ponto. As he returned the empty dish over the courtyard wall he said, 'Thank you Mam, have you got any more of that shaky stuff?'

As I have already said, Ponto was handy for running errands, fetching and carrying. The bier for funerals was kept in a parish 2 miles away. Ponto used to walk those 2 miles and come back pulling the bier. It was a strange sight to see along the Rabbit Lane, the little man pulling this carriage for transporting villagers from their cottages on their final journey to the churchyard.

Ponto had no sense of humour and could not differentiate between fantasy and reality. Most of us have suffered having our legs pulled in our time, and we brush off the ridiculous. Mrs Bayliss had a donkey, which broke its neck when it mysteriously fell in the parish quarry. The hobbledehoys at the pub spread the tale around that Ponto had pushed the donkey.

At Farmer Dunn's house that evening Ponto came to the back door. 'Master Dunn, you know me and I didn't push the donkey into the quarry,' he said with tears streaming down his bristly face. 'I wouldn't do such a thing. Mrs Bayliss is a friend of mine and, Master, would I harm her donkey?'

'Now look here, Ponto, take no notice. I know it's not true. The chaps at the pub – it's a pity they have nothing better to do but tell lies about you.'

Farmer Dunn's words partly satisfied the man from the cart house but there was more to come.

Jubilee, born on the Queen's Golden Jubilee in 1887, was chairman of the pig club, a sort of early National Health Scheme for pigs, an insurance against the loss of a bacon pig. His pig choked himself on an apple, a big apple, and died. Ponto got the blame and got the nickname 'Choke Pig'. Again there was no truth in the accusation but the nickname stuck and despite his employer's words to Ponto he was upset. I have seen Ponto chasing a group of hobbledehoys down the village street at The Cuckoo Pen as they chanted 'Choke Pig, Choke Pig'. Eventually Ponto left his native village to spend his evening hours and days at the workhouse.

Jubilee lived on keeping pigs and was the Sunday morning barber for the village. In summer time Jubilee scissored away at the farm men's scalps, short back and sides as tots of home-made wine went around the waiting customers. One chap who always fainted in the barber's chair had to be revived with brandy. Maybe Percy didn't relish Jubilee's plum Jerkum and the Agricultural Brandy (cider). A friendly spirit existed on those Sunday mornings when after the last man's hair had been trimmed they all walked around Jubilee's garden and admired his runner beans, his potatoes, strawberries, and so on until finally they finished up at the pigsty. Here Jubilee's latest Cottager's pig showed himself off to the spectators. The pig was always a cross between a Large White and a Large Black, which resulted in a sheeted pig, with patterns of blue on the white background, some round like half-crowns. If it was nearly time for Jasper the pig killer's visit, the men would guess the weight: sixteen score, seventeen score. Jubilee listened intently, but his mind was already made up having fattened so many pigs in his time.

TUSTIN THE COALMAN

It is hard to believe that a man earning less than £2 per week in the 1920s and '30s could save £2,000. But Jim Tustin and his wife did just that. They could have told William Cobbett about cottage economy (he had written a book with that title). Tustin and his wife were past masters at skimping and saving.

Tustin's main pleasure on Saturday afternoons was football matches involving the village team. It used to be threepence to cross the stile into the football field but Tustin's garden adjoined the pitch so he sat up in his plum tree to view the match. A coalman driving the horse and dray in the week, Sacco said that his dinner consisted of bread and pastry lard and cold tea without milk or sugar. Milk was a luxury which came in the form of skim milk, which he balanced in a can while he rode his bicycle back from an outlying farm on Sunday mornings.

A visit to Tustin's cottage was an eye-opener! The newspaper served as a tablecloth and the crevices in the window frames were stuffed with paper. 'Don't take thee hat off, we beunt proud folks in yer,' he said.

I asked him why he didn't mend the broken windows, and was told, 'Why should I spend my money on other folks' property?' I believe he paid half a crown a week rent!

'Dos't want a bit of my rhubarb?' he said.

I nodded and remarked on the size of the sticks.

'Oh,' he replied, 'I allus empties the closet bucket on it.'

Nothing wasted.

Tustin's stories of farm life in the last century told of hard work and hard living. He recalled sixteen weeks frost in February 1898! But other memories were not so harsh.

'I courted Polly the Gem for some time. You know her?'

I said, 'Yes, I knew Polly. She picked peas for us and Dad gave her a shilling too much when he paid her. She created! "Right's right and might's might and wrong is no man's right," she said when she returned the shilling.'

'Well, I went to Chapel one Sunday night along with Polly and took her on the path under the wood to where your land was, and her turned to me saying, "I don't wish to keep company with you any more, Jim." What do you think about that? Mind you her then went out along of Hubert and said as how he put his hand on her knee. She said, "I don't know what his intentions were."'

I smiled at old Tustin and said, 'Perhaps you were too slow for her. You married Doris then I believe.'

'Yes, and the folks at the pub said as I was obliged to but I knowed different. It was two years before the first baby was born. I knowed different.'

Tustin was, as he said, 'Eighty-seven next May if I be spared', and his tall, angular body was in good shape and he could still single mangold seedlings with his hoe. Mrs Tustin fired the wash-boiler with dry sprout stems, took home bits of soap from where she was charring for the wash, and kept Tustin going with vegetables from the garden and cheap butcher's meat.

SAPPER, A MASTER PLASTERER

On a main road in full view of The Cuckoo Pen and the hill stands a Victorian pebble-dashed cottage, a pretentious building with two great imitation stone balls on pillars, one each side of the entrance to the short driveway. This was Enfield Cottage, the home of master plasterer Sapper Greet, with ornate plasterwork and a pseudo-Norman arch to his barn. In the barn Sapper worked images in granite chippings, and made template patterns for all the wizardry of his trade. He made gravestones for the folk who could not afford the monumental masons. Sometimes the names of the deceased were cramped, but the stones showed a love for fellow men who had served in the army during the First World War.

Sapper was not satisfied with the site of the war memorial, so he built one in his yard, a masterpiece which was never erected. Oh, and other ex-servicemen dug the foundations on the village green one Saturday when everyone else was at the cricket match. But that was as far as it got. The concrete base remains as a memento.

What sort of a man was this artistic plasterer? Sapper was so skilled that he was engaged in the ornate plasterwork at the Shakespeare Memorial Theatre. Every morning a car came from Stratford some twenty-odd miles away to fetch Sapper. He and he alone had the artistry.

After serving as a Sapper in the First World War, he took to drink in a big way and this kept him poor. He could have been well off, he was in such demand.

I can picture Sapper on Sunday lunch time as he weaves his way down from the Plough and Harrow singing Mademoiselle from Armentiéres, Parlez Vous, mixing this with Pidgin French and his constant talk of Vin Blanc.

'Now,' he'd say to me, 'you of the Grammar School, *parlez vous*,' followed by the most amazing mixture of French and English, quite unintelligible.

To say Sapper was a poacher would be unkind, but this man had all the inbred skills necessary for taking game. His garden adjoined one field and then the pheasant-rich woodland of an estate. A row of withy trees marked his boundary fence. Here he fed the pheasants and at times baited them with raisins soaked in brandy, which gave the plasterer an easy pick of drunken birds.

Sapper was also an expert with the catapult. He practised his skill by shooting at a row of cocoa cans on the garden wall, but on nights after the cock pheasants let everyone know they had gone to roost Sapper took aim with his quiet missile, bringing down Sunday dinner or any other day's dinner. For ammunition he used leaden balls melted from sheet lead, a product of the roof gulleys on the Church or Mansion House.

To hit targets with a catapult is no mean feat but one day in the garden of Enfield Cottage Sapper showed me how accurate he could be with what he called his catty. Putting a candle on the garden wall he lit it, waited for the flames to flare up, then standing back about ten yards he fired a leaden ball at the flame, douting the candle.

Perhaps Sapper was wasted on the Royal Engineers; maybe he should have been a sniper.

Apart from his engagement at the Stratford Theatre, Sapper never worked on a Monday. He would say in his Gloucestershire burr, 'Why should a man go to work when he has the health and strength to stay in bed.'

The fact of the matter was the plasterer had heavy drinking sessions at the weekend and it took Monday to recover. Apart from the drink Sapper did enjoy his pipe of tobacco and what a pipe! He smoked a big cherry pipe which held the best part of half an ounce of tobacco. At the Plough and Harrow some unsuspecting gentleman would hand his tobacco pouch to this plasterer and find that the pouch was all but empty afterwards.

If there was anything special about Sapper it was the way he improvised. Nothing stopped him doing what he wanted to do. In the twenties there was a surge of council house building. Sapper contracted for plastering the inside, and rough casting the outside.

It was high summer. A row of council houses was being built in a village 10 miles from Sapper's home. For building workers to sleep overnight in houses under construction was commonplace. In one of the row of these houses Sapper had partly finished the plasterwork. The glass was not in the windows but Sapper decided that he could spend the night there. The particular property had been allotted to an undertaker who stored some coffins in the front room.

Walking back from the pub in the village having had his night cap of local cider, Sapper arrived at the council house. He studied the scene. Deciding that the draught from the unglazed windows would be cool by morning light, he lined a coffin with his overcoat, used his tool-bag as a pillow and, lying comfortably, he was soon asleep. Early morning, before daylight, a police constable on his round was checking up. He shone his torch through the unglazed window to see a man's body in the coffin. He blew his whistle, startling the plasterer who sat up from his bed. Sapper then told the PC exactly what he thought, ending with these words, 'I shall report you to your Superior Officer for robbing a working man of a night's sleep.'

The year was 1923 and the coal-house was a low-ceilinged, dark room where fourteen cats had their quarters. Dad decided that we needed what was called a drawing room. Sapper did the work. The higher ceiling was fixed by more rafters with lath nailed to them. No fancy plasterboard was used; the real plaster ceiling was done the hard way.

Two bags of cow hair from the Argentine were beaten and fluffed up by Jack, Sapper's labourer, referred to by Sapper as his Stiff Un.

Sapper slaked the lump lime in a barrel until the mixture boiled. This was known as running the putty. Mixed with the cow hair, Sapper's plaster stuck to and between the laths like glue. The smooth surface was perfect, so were the picture-railed and chair-railed walls. The chimney, built in brickwork, was to be plastered on the inside several feet from where the fireplace was to be. Sapper insisted that the chimney was to be pargeted so he sent Jack out into the yard to meet the incoming milking cows. Jack, with a bucket, collected enough fresh cow manure for the job. Sapper mixed this with plaster to prevent the plasterwork from cracking, one of his old methods.

Every Sunday on his way from the Plough and Harrow to Enfield Cottage, Sapper never failed to stand at attention for a while and salute the concrete base where his war memorial should have stood. The finished cross with a laurel wreath in granite chippings was in Sapper's yard with a Union Jack partly covering the memorial.

One wonders what went through the minds of the ex-servicemen, Snob, Whistler and the rest, who supported the plasterer when the memorial was built in the village pound.

Sapper's wartime service didn't finish at the Armistice. He was a soldier to the end. At a neighbouring village the pub landlord said as the plasterer came into the bar, 'Here comes the man who won the war.'

Never again did Sapper enter that inn. But as his age prevented him doing work and earning money, he rarely visited the inns in the area anymore. Instead Sapper brewed home-made wine.

His damson trees in the garden hedge were a pretty sight in the spring and the blue fruits provided the ingredients for Sapper's wine making. After a year's keeping this wine laced with rice was powerful stuff. Frank Bird was making some very good cider from the real cider apples of the farms. He sold four-and-a-half gallon barrels to his customers and Sapper was never out of cider.

Home-made wine or home-made cider can have disastrous effects when too much is consumed. Sapper used to brag that some days he drank eight pints. Stories are told of Delirium Tremens or 'Blue

Devils' appearing when too much alcohol has been drunk. I was always sceptical about such stories but it happened in Carrants Field opposite Enfield Cottage. Joe the market gardener had sprouts planted in that field, about 5 acres. It was Christmas time and he had already picked over his crop. Sapper drank a quantity of his damson wine followed by a few pints of Frank Bird's cider. He went to bed at 10 o'clock. His son-in-law Bill was staying overnight, and all was quiet for a peaceful Christmas.

At 1 o'clock in the morning Sapper went downstairs in his nightshirt and slippers. Blue Devils 'appeared' across the road in Joe's field. Grabbing a carving knife the plasterer ran across the road shouting, 'I'll get you buggers.'

Then through the gate into the field he chased them up and down the sprout rows in his nightshirt on that cold frosty night when the leaves of the plants were covered with hoarfrost.

For a while Sapper ran after the elusive devils until Bill came out partly dressed and confronted him. Bill wouldn't hear one word from him and said, 'Sapper, up those stairs and back to bed.'

And the plasterer did just that.

WILFRED AND CLAUD

On the outskirts of The Cuckoo Pen, right on the village and county boundary, a solicitor's son from the Welsh Borders rented a 250 acre farm. The farmhouse was supposed to be haunted and was once exorcized by the Bishop. The house was a good example of Elizabethan architecture. In front, a double gateway stood between great stone balls on pillars. Some folk who knew little of the history of the area called it The Manor but the true Manor lay at the other end of The Cuckoo Pen.

Wilfred, the college-trained, spoilt son of a solicitor farmed well for a while during the First World War. He had a fine team of horses, useful implements and a herd of beef cattle. Wilfred brought with him from the Borders two men, Tom the carter and Alec the stockman.

Tom was proud of his team but soon found that Wilfred was spending too much time at the Plough and Harrow. His friendship with Claud didn't help. Claud came to The Cuckoo Pen during the war, no doubt to escape from military service. He had a small-holding down by the brook where men worked part-time for him, being handsomely paid and with plenty of cider.

I can picture the scene at haymaking when Wilfred rode on one mowing machine pulled by two horses and Tom the carter on another. They were mowing The Slad, a 25 acre field adjoining the next village. At 1 o'clock, dinner time, the two pairs of horses were tied up under an oak tree. Tom and his Gaffer were eating their bread and cheese in the shade. Men and horses had been circling The Slad since 5 o'clock that morning and more than half the mowing was done.

Wilfred said, 'I could fancy some of that beer, cold from the cellar of the Queen Elizabeth.'

Tom responded, 'But Gaffer, we have a jar of cider cool under the hedge.'

Wilfred then took his carter with him across the fields to the Queen Elizabeth in the next parish, leaving the horses under the oak tree in The Slad. 'We won't stop long, Tom, just a couple of drinks then back to the mowing.'

Tom thought, 'I've heard these tales before.'

And sure enough Wilfred fell in with a neighbouring farmer and master and man were there until closing time at 10 o'clock. It seemed that Tom had more concern in getting the haymaking done than the spoilt solicitor's son.

Tom told me that if they had stayed and worked that afternoon the mowing would have been finished, but the two beer-fuddled men did not collect their horses until dark had fallen that June night, taking them to the stable at what some called Manor Farm.

The haymaking at Wilfred's farm could be described as a jamboree. Men came from neighbouring villages to take part, a mixture of old men and hobbledehoys who came to work in the hayfields. You see, Wilfred was generous to the extreme. He killed a pork pig, and had it cooked in the big kitchen of the farmhouse by his wife for the men. Baskets of pork and bread were ferried from the farmhouse to the hayfield by an old fellow named Tetbury Ted who lived in the saddle room. This, with ample cider, tempted the folk of The Cuckoo Pen to make hay with Wilfred.

By the time the big rick was finished by the lane at the bottom of The Slad it was beginning to get dark. Wilfred sent Ted down to the farmhouse for more cider.

Wilf's wife Kathleen said, 'But Ted, it's getting dark, why does the Master want more cider at this time of night?'

'I don't know, Mam,' he replied. 'But that's my orders.'

Ted hung the jar of cider from the hames of the trace horse and mounted, jogging through the dark to the hayfield where the haymakers were having a kind of party, described to me by Alec, Wilfred's cowman.

'We sung and we danced around that rick the best part of the night. Some, overcome by the cider, slept in the hay, but the hollering, the shouting, and the singing rang from The Slad. Anyone passing would have thought we had gone mad. Perhaps we were. Twenty-five acres of hay went into that rick. Oh, it was a big rick built by young Tom.'

Wilfred's wife Kathleen employed young Nellie Hawker as general maid. Nellie was the daughter of Fred Hawker who had been cowman for Tom Dunn. Wilfred had an industrious wife, a worker who tried unsuccessfully to keep her husband on the straight and narrow. She galloped through the housework with Nellie, never still, always on the go.

One morning Nellie was on her knees scrubbing the kitchen floor. Kathleen went to-ing and fro-ing, and twice she stepped on Nellie's hands. The third time it happened Nellie caught her by the ankle and brought her down in a sort of Rugby tackle.

'What *are* you doing Nellie? You could have hurt me.'

'Well keep off my hands then, Ma'am,' Nellie replied.

Nellie worked there for a couple of years and said that they had rabbit for a meal every day bar one for all that time. It was the case of: Rabbits young and rabbits old, rabbits hot or rabbits cold, rabbits tender, rabbits tough. Now I think I've had enough.

Apart from these minor details Nellie was happy working for Kathleen. She told me how she fed the poultry, collected the eggs and that the whole gaggle of geese would trot down from the farm to the stubble fields in autumn following the gander. A sight, she said, to remember.

Wilfred bought an Overland car during the First World War and he and Claud made evening trips to Cheltenham, visiting the theatre and pubs. On one of these outings, going through a village with lots of S-bends, Claud announced to Wilfred, 'Where the hell do you think we are going?'

He got the reply, 'Cheltenham, of course, you fool.'

'Don't know who is the biggest fool, Wilfred, 'cause we are on the way home.'

The car had spun round in the road on an S-bend. But in those days with little traffic on the road Wilfred did use the lanes as a racetrack. The two goggled men fancied themselves as being at Brooklands Racetrack. Waste of money, waste of time – that motto seemed to sum up this young farmer.

'What about planting the wheat, Wilfred?' Tom asked his boss one October day and got the reply, 'We don't plant corn on the Welsh Borders until the spring.'

Tom persuaded his Gaffer to get some seed. He and Alec planted and harrowed in 15 acres in Cinder Meadow but it was a hard battle for young Tom to get things done on the farm. He told me Wilfred was in to anything foolhardy, but work was different.

Claud knew very little of horticulture but Jubilee told him when and what to plant on his 5 acres and Frank Bird who kept a horse and dray at the Plough and Harrow took Claud's produce to the local market.

A picture of Claud remains vividly in my mind. He was an unusually tall, ungainly man with ginger hair and a moustache. He tried in his dress to ape a middle-class countryman and succeeded in a way. His long spindly legs were encased in buttoned-up leggings over immaculate breeches and he wore made-to-measure boots. In fact, it all appeared to be made to measure, including his hacking jacket. I recall a kind of Sherlock Holmes hat. Claud sometimes rode one of Wilfred's horses, but was mostly seen on a green Sunbeam bicycle. He married Sophie, the elder daughter of Mr and Mrs George Summers.

The second winter Wilfred farmed the 250 acres proved to be severe. The snow covered the lane, making travelling difficult for horses and men. One morning Wilfred and Claud woke up to a white world. Tom and Alec were engaged in chaff cutting in the big barn with an oil engine. They had seen to their animals, the horses and cows. Caleb's blacksmith's shop adjoined Wilfred's farm buildings. In the stable the farmer and his market gardener friend sat on a bench smoking what were commonly called cheroots.

'Tell you what, Wilfred, if we took the wheels off your trap we could use it as a sledge, the springs would act as runners over the snow.'

Claud's idea seemed plausible to Wilfred so they sought Caleb's advice, asking him to take the wheels off the trap. That was soon accomplished and the three men carried the light vehicle on to the snow in the yard.

Now Wilfred had a very high-stepping cob named Polly. 'Fetch Polly out of the nag stable, Tom,' Wilfred called from the barn, 'and put the gears on her.'

'You beunt gwain to town in this weather be ya?' Tom replied.

Claud said with a grin, 'We are going sledging.'

Tom put Polly between the shafts of the trap and the two men took off down the village heading for the Beckford Inn.

'What's wrong with Frank Bird's beer?' Alec said to Tom, who replied, 'Tis whisky they be after. Frank don't have a spirit licence.'

Down the village street some families were shovelling snow from their paths. Stodge was helping Cyril to clear the snow from the path to the Church. No one had gone to work, except to feed the animals. Joe and Lofty had done a couple of hours sprout picking, but had now gone back home.

When the home-made sledge came past the Plough and Harrow Jubilee declared to Frank Bird, 'What sights you see when you haven't got your gun!'

Schoolboys followed the sledge, housewives looked from cottage windows and wondered whether they were seeing things. Blenheim and Harry stood in Tom Dunn's farm gateway waving to Wilfred's outfit. Blenheim shouted, 'I'm damned if I didn't think it was Father Christmas.'

Down the road Polly pulled the sledge, the schoolboys followed to the end of The Cuckoo Pen. Folk from the next village down Rabbit Lane looked doubtfully at what they saw.

At the inn Fred Pope put Polly in one of his stables leaving the sledge outside. He knew that these men would drink a couple of bottles of whisky and treat all and sundry to drinks. Fred Pope welcomed them with open arms and his customers came out on to the snow to see the home-made sledge.

At dinner time the snow was still falling. Men who called at the inn for drinks were amused at the sledge outside. Wilfred and Claud had drunk one bottle of whisky and made a start on another. It always happened that when the customers at the inn knew that the two toffs from The Cuckoo Pen were there the word got around. 'Free drinks for all' was the usual thing.

The paraffin lamp in front of the inn shone on a wintery scene, but things were beginning to change. Locals said the wind had veered round to the south, and that little trickles of water were coming off the roof. Wilfred and Claud were warned that if they didn't go home soon the snow would be melted off Rabbit Lane.

At 10 o'clock Fred Pope closed the bar. The snow had melted. 'You can leave Polly in the stable and fetch your trap tomorrow.' These words of the landlord didn't encourage these two men on their walk back those 2½ miles home.

'This story ull get into *The Cheil*,' one farmer said to another, 'the piece in the local paper when news of something strange is reported.'

'They be only two overgrown schoolkids,' another observed. 'They will remember sledging down Rabbit Lane for a long time I reckon.'

Next morning Tom and Alec loaded two trap wheels on to a muck cart pulled by one of Wilfred's cart horses. They were on their way to the Beckford Inn. Wilfred asked Caleb to go with them to put the wheels back on the trap.

'We shall all be in *The Cheil*,' Tom said. 'And I notice the Gaffer's not coming with us today.'

'Thick yuds them two gentlemen have got today I reckon,' was Alec's comment.

With the wheels fixed on the trap and Polly between the shafts, Tom and Caleb were soon trotting back to The Cuckoo Pen. They left Alec to take the muck cart back home. As he said he always was left with the worst job.

Through the Seasons

THE PEA-PICKERS

The folk who lived around The Cuckoo Pen would have been so much poorer if Farmer Dunn and his neighbours hadn't grown crops of peas. Harry, Dunn's carter, planted the early varieties about Candlemas, 2 February, and these were fit to pick in early June. Like the hop-pickers of Kent, pea-picking was a paid holiday during the years between the wars.

From the middle of May a steady stream of itinerant pickers arrived. These folk were a mixture of humanity. One man had been a successful Chartered Accountant, a Londoner who was just known as Cock. The vagrant men often chose to be known by where they came from: Manchester, Stafford, Brummie or Devon. These folk who tramped the roads from one workhouse to the next provided a reservoir of workers. Nicknamed 'Gentlemen of the Road', many had fought in the First World War. They came early to stake their claim on the barns, bothies, stables and cowsheds around The Cuckoo Pen, although some preferred bivouacs, and put up tents made out of sacking under the hawthorn hedges. They had spent the winter in doss-houses, casual wards and lodging houses, some had even been in jail for petty offences, and they arrived lean and bedraggled. By September, however, the outdoor life in the fields, and wholesome food, gave them a more healthy bloom.

As sure as the cuckoo came in April, Scottie and Darkie arrived in May. It's anyone's guess where they met on their route to their usual quarters in the old thatched sheep barn known as the Cross Barn, an historic building that shepherds had used as lambing pens for generations. The shepherd had lambed his ewes in the building in February and March, and Dunn's men had cleaned the earthen floor. The great elm beams had Roman numerals carved into the woodwork where they joined the cross timbers. In years gone by some carpenter had laid out those timbers and fitted the joints before erecting the skeleton of the sheep barn. Dunn's shepherd used hurdles to make little maternity pens for the expectant woolly mothers, and here he practised his art of midwifery. The orphan lamb was introduced to a foster mother, the ewe with no appetite was enticed with ivy from the hedgerow. A whole history of shepherding had been enacted between the four walls of the barn.

Scottie and Darkie arrived at the barn below The Cuckoo Pen having parted company the previous September. Darkie had overwintered in London, selling matches on the streets. How Scottie survived the winter we never knew. I'm sure this tall, elegant Scot would not demean himself by trading as a street hawker.

Like hoards of men on the road, these two men were ex-service men. 'Your Country Needs You' Lord Kitchener had said, but unfortunately not when the war was over.

Darkie had served in the Royal Engineers, a navvy who was a glutton for work but on his demob he took to drink, did a few jobs on the sewers in East Anglia, then drifted.

Scottie had been Chief Engineer on one of the ocean liners. Then he became hooked on gambling. Although he didn't waste his money on drink, for he was a staunch teetotaller, it melted at the bookmakers like butter in the sun. He was a striking figure, over six foot tall, upright, his grey hair tidy and still showing traces of the redhead he had been as a young man. Apart from his waxed moustache, he was clean shaven. Scottie smoked an old meerschaum pipe and walked, or marched with a cane. Every year the ageing showed a little more but by September Scottie would be fit to survive yet another winter. A philosopher, a great talker, with a knowledge of religion and politics, Scottie held court on the village Cross where some of his contemporaries met on Sunday.

In the Cross Barn Scottie made a couple of pens with the shepherd's hurdles and he and Darkie took boltings of straw for their separate beds. Over his own bed Scottie chalked on a beam 'He Who Steals my Purse Steals Trash'.

The travellers always brought a few bits and pieces with them to the barn – a broken mirror placed on a ledge between the beams, a bucket for water, two billycans made from cocoa tins and wire handles, a well-stained Blue Bird toffee tin which served as a frying-pan, and a couple of saucepans.

Out in the orchard at the back of the barn under the churchyard wall and near a Peasgood Nonsuch apple tree was the place where the men from the barn had their fire. Scottie did the cooking, and watched over saucepans of potatoes and green peas as they boiled. The Ship's Engineer would sit on a hamper smoking his pipe as Darkie brought armfuls of wood from the hedgerow. Corned beef was the men's meat dish. They cooked it in the toffee tin-cum-frying-pan. The billycans for the tea were twirled around to cool the liquid before condensed milk was added. Cyril, looking over the churchyard wall from his mowing, remarked, 'You chaps live like fighting cocks. The cooking's giving me an appetite for my tea.'

Scottie, never at a loss for words, said, 'Sir, didn't my friend and I fight for our country? I served in the Merchant Navy dodging the Kaiser's U-boats, Darkie in France with the Engineers.'

'Oh, we are glad to see you every year and would welcome you in St Luke's Church on Sunday.'

'In Church? Oh, I'm become an agnostic of late, Sir. We tramp the roads, a life that does not tend towards the Church. Yet I can quote the Scriptures and we have much in common with the man from Galilee; no roof over his head.'

As they waited for the pea pods to fill up, Scottie would walk the road past Coney Burrows to the early pea field every evening, a distinguished figure. Meanwhile Darkie, earning a few shillings working on Frank Bird's garden at the Plough, would then spend it on beer.

Farmer Dunn would put up a notice in his first pea field on a Saturday which read: PEA-PICKERS WANTED ON MONDAY. He employed Old Jubilee to weigh the peas and give a cheque, a metal token, to the pickers for every 40 lb bag picked. He arrived on the field at 5 o'clock on the Monday morning. To east and west, north and south the news got around: Farmer Dunn has started pea-picking. Scottie and Darkie had already filled two bags though; they had been the first in the field.

The pea-pickers, nomads like Scottie, Darkie and the rest, the Loveridges, the Orchards and the Lees all of the gipsy folk, all got on well together, and with the local women. But the notice in the pea field was also seen by a group of Diddicoys, scrap-iron jacks who passed in their lorries. Soon they were with Tom Dunn, asking permission to pull in to the Stone Bridge Ground, a one-acre field adjoining the brook. Permission granted, the word went round and all the scrap-iron lorries came and filled the little field. Their women folk went pea-picking but were not welcomed by the others. Jubilee, who gave out the tokens in the pea field, said that the men with the lorries were, to put it mildly, light-fingered. Soon they had crossed the brook and made a track to the railway siding, stealing sacks of coal from a ten-ton truck. Their Lurcher dogs worked the adjoining fields catching hares and rabbits. Nothing was safe in that area of land below The Cuckoo Pen.

Another trick they played was to promise money, but then not pay up.

'Have you scrap iron, Sir? We will pay you well for any,' they asked Farmer Dunn.

Tom Dunn replied, 'I have a few old implements on the hill but it needs two horses and a wagon to bring it down. Harry may be persuaded to fetch it if you pay him.'

Harry took the cart track with horses and wagons to Great Hill barn, accompanied by two of the Diddicoys.

'We will cross your hand with silver, Carter, if you help us load the iron.'

Old mowing machines, binders, and ploughs were broken by the

Diddicoys' sledgehammers. Harry sweated all that afternoon lifting iron on to his wagon, which was then unloaded on to the lorries. But there was no silver for Harry, and no money for Tom Dunn either.

The Diddicoys stayed on and their camp at Stone Bridge came to be permanent. When PC Smith had evidence about the stolen coal he told them to go or else. But the women and the men surrounded the constable and he could not get a word in edgeways. Fortunately they moved off and Tom Dunn learnt his lesson about letting Diddicoys on to his fields.

On Friday night at Dunn's farm the cheques that the pickers had earned were changed. Each little tin disc with Dunn's initials on could be exchanged for one shilling. Later, at the Plough the voices of the men and women were oiled. Songs from the First World War were sung, and the village below The Cuckoo Pen rang with music.

As the pea-picking season progressed the population of the village increased by more than a hundred and Frank Bird's public house was lively both inside and out. Most of the travellers sat outside on seats in Frank's orchard. Many of the pickers had several subs during the week and could not survive until Friday. Tom Dunn paid out the shillings for each cheque counter exchanged and when he was short of change he knew that Frank Bird at the Plough and Harrow had the money which the pickers had earned. Over to the pub Tom's son was sent with £5 notes for Frank to exchange for 100 shillings. It was a very civilized way of exchanging money.

At closing time the pea-pickers made their way to their quarters. The long lingering 'Good nights' from one to another going on for an hour.

'Good night Brummie.'

'Good night Manchester. God Bless. Now, what I said, no hard feelings my friend.'

'That's alright, God bless. Don't be late in the morning.'

The men would part, then think again and walk towards each other.

'Good night. You remember what I said Brummie. No hard feelings. God bless you, sleep well.'

'Right Manchester. Good night to you.'

Back in the old stable by the fowl house Joe the Doings was snoring away in the manger. He had come home early from the pub, a bit peart. Annie Shaw, a lady who had travelled from Lancashire for the pea-picking, sang her way down the street into Dunn's yard with Cock.

'Good night Cock.'

'Good night my friend,' came the reply as Cock made for the granary steps.

From the manger, Annie Shaw's billet, came the sound of snoring and Joe the Doings sat up, the moonlight shining through the half stable-door giving enough light for Annie to know that a man was in her bed. Her screams were heard through the village. Screams as if murder was being committed. Joe the Doings lay back in the manger.

From the farmhouse Farmer Dunn heard Annie's screams. He put his trousers over his nightshirt, slipped on an overcoat and in his leather slippers went downstairs.

'Oh, Tom. Oh, Tom. Be careful, it sounds like a fight,' Mary Dunn pleaded. 'Be careful.'

'Now then, what's the trouble?' Farmer Dunn asked sharply of the group around the stable.

'That man's in my bed, Sir. In my bed!'

Joe the Doings sat up and Farmer Dunn told him, 'Now Joe, get out of Annie's bed. There's lots of room in the granary for you.'

Peace finally resumed that Friday night. The men respected Annie Shaw.

There was great excitement on a Monday morning one year when the word went to Tom Dunn's house that one of the pea-picker's wives was in labour and the District Nurse was called.

George Orchard's wife, Gipsy Lill, the daughter of a real gipsy, lay on a bunk-bed in a tent close by the Church. George was one of the travelling men. Both were dark and swarthy and the parents of two lovely little boys.

The District Nurse arrived to find that everything for the birth was ready. Outside the tent a cauldron of water boiled. Mrs

Orchard's baby was born in Church Close, a lovely little boy of 7 lb. That evening a group of gipsies came from the pea field with presents for the Orchard family. They were led by Old Alec Loveridge, a giant of a man who had a family living in a caravan pulled by a skewbald horse, a caravan weighed down with silver and brass. A healthy birth had taken place in Church Close. I wonder if ever a child had been born before in that parkland field where the oak trees have stood since the first Queen Elizabeth was on the throne, where spring waters from the hill have run crystal clear to the moat pond, and where an ancestor of Blenheim had warded off the press gang with his scythe.

The birth in Church Close was followed by a death in a caravan in that field. It was little Stafford, who lived with a colony of cats in a caravan and worked for Tom Dunn. He settled in the field under The Cuckoo Pen, having come from the Potteries, and lived there for years. Stafford liked his beer but as old Blenheim used to say, 'He'd only got to drink one pint and see someone else drink another and he was drunk.'

Stafford slipped away at the age of sixty-five and Sacco had the job of burying him. After the funeral Sacco seemed upset by the undertaker, although they were great friends. After a few jars of cider he finally said, 'What do you think you were doing putting little Stafford in a box measuring six foot three inches when Stafford was but five foot and a tater. It's not on, you know. I had to dig that hole much longer than necessary.'

Revd Vernon had a surprise too, thinking that few folk would be in church. The building was actually full. Stafford had his friends who remembered him. He dug gardens for widows, bought sweets for children, helped Cyril to mow the churchyard. Stafford was a kind little man who had lived among the folk of The Cuckoo Pen as a sort of oracle, a talisman.

One picker we knew as Soldier. His khaki uniform from the First World War marked him as an ex-serviceman. He arrived with a little boy of about four years old. His wife had died and left Soldier with the boy. They were a sad sight as they bedded down in one of Dunn's pigsties. Soldier was very emphatic that the little boy, named Peter, was well mannered. When Mary Dunn gave him some sweets, Soldier, in a flash, said, 'Peter. You just say thank you to Godly Folk and Gentry.'

Under the granary an open shed was the summer home for Little Titch and a whiskery old man who had an Old English sheep dog. They stayed together as friends and Titch and the old man picked together, drank together and ate their food together in the yard outside the shed.

Titch would sit on a wooden box in the yard cutting his corns and toe nails with a shut knife while the old man drummed up the tea in the billycans. Not the most industrious pickers, they rarely started work until 10 o'clock while Scottie and Darkie were in the fields before daylight. Where the two men came from no one knew, and no one questioned.

The most upright man among the pea-pickers was an ex-corporal from the Gloucestershire Regiment, Corporal Reed, known as the Corporal. He arrived at The Cuckoo Pen and found a lodging in a barn previously belonging to David Drinkwater. The two ladies at the black and white Elizabethan house befriended the Corporal, one the widow of David Drinkwater and the other her spinster sister. The Corporal had been on the ground staff at Cheltenham College Cricket Ground and knew how to prepare a wicket – when he was sober! This man had boasted that he had been General Allenby's personal bodyguard when he freed Jerusalem in 1917, but drink had been his downfall. Apart from his spell in preparing wickets, the Corporal was no mean gardener and he found work tidying the gardens of the village.

The village cricket captain was an ex-army officer. Raymond was a very good batsman who had played for a county second eleven. He had Christian principles, a zest for life, and great compassion for the underdog.

At one cricket meeting, chaired by Cyril, lengthy discussions were held. Raymond said how delighted he was over Corporal

Reed's well-prepared wicket, and he proposed letting him live in the new pavilion as his lodgings were very poor, and he could look after the cricket gear.

'Have you seen the state of the barn where he lives? He's an untidy, dirty chap who we can't have in the pavilion. What will the visiting teams think?'

This outburst from Frank Bird set the meeting alight. Some supported Raymond, but the majority agreed how unwise it was to let the Corporal into the pavilion. The idea was dropped.

On Whit Monday an all-day match against Ragley Park was held. At 11 o'clock the players took the field, with Corporal as umpire. He was about half-drunk.

Now, the previous Saturday the visiting team had complained that the pitch was only 20 yards long instead of 22 yards long. It was a mistake that the Corporal had made, and it had been chewed over in the Plough and Harrow all the week.

At the start of the Whit Monday match Cyril came on to the pitch and said to Raymond, 'I hope it's a 22 yard wicket today.'

The Corporal lunged at Cyril, then let out some of the foulest language ever heard at The Cuckoo Pen.

'I'm not going to be sworn at,' exclaimed Cyril. 'Raymond, dismiss the man.'

Raymond turned to the ex-corporal asking him to apologize to Cyril.

'What! Me, apologize to that yellow-belly who led a sheltered life during the war. Me, who faced the enemy.'

He walked from the field, and Cyril umpired the match. The confrontation between the Corporal and the ex-insurance bachelor was something never forgotten among the Ragley team.

THE SYMPHONY OF
THRESHING

No one at The Cuckoo Pen in the 1920s thought of threshing as anything other than a dusty, dirty job which made the days seem endless. In retrospect, there was music and rhythm when a steam engine turned a threshing machine, with all its little belts and pulleys. In those far-off days when the farm revolved around horsepower and manpower a steam engine was exciting.

The word got around that Tom Dunn was having his ricks threshed and that Harry, Blenheim and young Jim had gone to the village to fetch the threshing tackle. Boys on holiday from school at Christmas waited at the crossroads for the caravan of horses and tackle to arrive. Harry came in sight at the head of the outfit. His two horses were pulling what is known as a portable steam engine. Blenheim followed with two more horses pulling the threshing drum. Young Jim had one horse in the shafts with the straw tier. Behind them Joe North, the engine driver, pushed his bicycle; he had just completed four days threshing at a farm in the next village.

Joe had to set the engine and machine alongside the first of Tom Dunn's ricks. The horses scauted and slipped as they pulled the engine up the incline into the rick-yard, although the threshing machine and straw tier were no trouble for them.

Boys stood around anxious for tomorrow and Dunn's annual thresh. They would take part, mainly by killing rats and mice with their nut sticks. In days before television or wireless threshing was a part of the social life of the village. Men and boys worked as a team; it was like a theatre, with the actors corduroyed and rosy-faced on the rick-yard stage.

Joe North was particular to set his machine correctly. A spirit-level on the side of the threshing drum confirmed the accuracy of his setting. A block of wood here and there under a jacked-up wheel resulted in the drum being dead-level.

Next morning when Joe North arrived in the rick-yard at 6 o'clock, the yard was still as black as the ace of spades. Harry had hauled a cart load of coal and wood for firing the steam engine. Joe walked around his black horse, as he called it, with a carbide lamp off his bicycle, stuffing kindling wood and small steam coal into the firebox. The steam gauge stood at zero. As the pressure registered on the steam gauge it rose a little and the smoke came black from the long chimney. Joe waited, then put on a bit more coal until the pressure of steam came nearly to working point. At 7 o'clock, and still dark, Joe blew blasts with the steam whistle. The men began to arrive, and the boys with their sticks.

Thirty minutes later, in the half light, Harry had taken the thatch from the first rick, assisted by Sacco. This plasterer was always game for a few days threshing in winter and Tom Dunn was glad of him.

The long belt from steam engine to threshing machine began to turn. The engine responded to Joe's steady push on the regulator, all pulleys and cogs turned: chuff, chuff, chub. Steam and smoke wafted over the rick-yard. The percussion of steam, with its gentle rhythm, began. The drum inside the threshing machine began to turn slowly with mellow bass notes: more, more, more. As the speed increased the straw tier answered, a discordant clack, clack, clack, but the little pulleys whined from contralto to tenor and unoiled cogs squealed soprano. The pace increased. Harry and Lofty were on the rick tossing the sheaves to Sacco who, with a bone-handled shut knife, cut the strings, dropping the sheaves in front of Berty, Joe's mate.

The sound of the drum was now in a different key. As the drum threshed the wheat noises like a hailstorm came in sharp contrast to the steady more, more, more.

Joe North walked around the machine, squirting oil from his can into the axles of pulley wheels. He kept an eye on the steam gauge and with a flat stick put dodment or congealed grease from wagon axles on to the big belt to prevent slipping. The join on the belt made of leather thongs, laces through holes, flopped every time it passed either the fly wheel of the engine or the pulley wheel of the machine. At the one end of the machine where the wheat came down a spout into the great 2¼ cwt sack Lofty, who left his market garden for the threshing, wheeled the full sacks to the granary.

Tom Dunn let the wheat from this spout fall through his fingers assessing the quality. He filled a little bag to send to the merchants. At the other end Caleb pitched the heavy boltings of straw to Ponto and Blenheim, who built the straw rick. Young Jim carried the chaff to the barn and kept the water barrels full. A half barrel stood separately where the Iron Horse sucked its water and where the boys drowned mice. They killed the rats with their sticks.

How glad the men were for their half-hour break when 10 o'clock came. At 10.30 prompt Joe North blew that steam whistle which seemed to echo all around the village green. Jim, who carried the chaff and the water at a previous threshing of barley, was a spectacle. He wore a red Salvation Army jersey and the barley hales stuck to the jersey and Jim walked around the rick-yard looking like a hedgehog.

Blenheim was forever reminiscing at dinner time as the men sat on the sacks of wheat in the granary. He spoke of a woman who cut the strings from the sheaves in the Squire's time. She said to the Squire, 'That's a good sample of wheat you got there, Sir.'

He replied, 'Yes. If you can carry a sack to your cottage you can have one.'

Old Betsy got the men to put one on her back and she carried it about 50 yards down the road.

And what about Fred Hawker's father. He carried two sacks on his back for a bet, won his bet and ruptured himself in the process.

The first rick was finished at twilight, at 4.30; the rats had been killed; and as the engine slowed down the machine spoke in a tired tone: more, more, more. Then it stopped. Joe's engine hissed, telling him 'Knocking-off time'.

THE MOP FAIR AND THE FIRST CONKER

In Ecclesiastes, Chapter 3, we read 'To everything there is a season and a time to every purpose under the Heaven'. Verse 4 continues, 'A time to weep and a time to laugh; a time to mourn and a time to dance'. At The Cuckoo Pen the children had their seasons too. Tops were in, but hoops were out; paper chases, known as Hare and Hounds, were in during The Cuckoo Pen holidays, as well as tip cat on summer evenings and hobbledy honkers in November. The hurdy-gurdy man came some Saturdays, and at Christmas Sunday school parties, carol singing and the drum and fife band from town came, known as the Tabber and Tut. The Mop Fair in the nearby town was held in October. On other occasions a travelling cine man put on a show in a marquee at Laughing Tom's farm.

One often hears today of adults and children becoming bored, and having nothing to do. The children of The Cuckoo Pen were never bored, they had probably never even heard of the expression. In retrospect it's quite a marvel how we were entertained and how we entertained ourselves in a village without television, radio and with just a very rare visit to the cinema in town.

There is truth in the saying 'a shilling, a knife and a piece of string and one can cut, tie and buy'. What we concocted with our penknives was legion. A forked stick and a length of catapult elastic and with pebbles from the stream as ammunition, we competed with other boys aiming at targets of cocoa cans. Spinning tops could be bought at the village shop for a penny. The tall flyers were favourites with the boys. We made our whips from ash sticks and pudding string. They looked spectacular as we whipped them up and down the village street. Some were painted in bright colours, others we coloured ourselves, making rings of chalk on the flat top. So the hours passed in the spring. In every farmyard and at the blacksmith's there was a graveyard of broken old implements. The wheels from corn drills made excellent hoops and by getting the blacksmith to bend a length of half inch round bar to form a hook these hooks with the drill wheels made a wonderful toy. We ran up and down the road with the hook on the hoop, no need to use a stick.

By sharpening a three inch stick at both ends and using a two foot stick to strike it the result was a tip cat, which when it was struck would fly up in the air. The art was to hit it in the air. This could be dangerous if there were windows nearby!

Milly Bostock or Bunch, whatever name suited her, was a lady who cared for the old, the infirm and the poor. At a farm sale she bought a bath chair. It was made of basketwork, two wheels at the back and a little wheel at the front, with a long handle to steer it by. Milly bought this chair for the use of anyone in The Cuckoo Pen who needed it, folk unable to walk, and it was stored in Tom Dunn's granary. Jonathan and my brother were twelve years old and I was eleven. One of us suggested taking the chair high up on the hill just below the beech trees of The Cuckoo Pen and then taking turns riding it down the hill. It was such fun, but that was not why Milly had bought the chair. Two of us were coming down a steep slope. I was trying to steer but we hit a large oak tree and the little wheel came from its axle. The axle was broken through.

Old Caleb was a useful friend. At his blacksmith's shop we boys, rather downcast at this point, persuaded him to shut weld the axle. As the two pieces of metal became first red hot then white hot we watched Caleb fuse them together on the anvil with blows from his heavy hammer. Jonathan, the eldest of our trio, asked him, 'How much do we owe you?' The answer half a crown meant that we each paid ten-pence in old money. The repaired chair was put back in Tom Dunn's granary, never to be used as a kind of go-cart again. No one ever knew and whether some invalid from The Cuckoo Pen ever rode in that chariot I'll never know. Boys will be boys.

The hurdy-gurdy man started his music near the village Cross, then up outside the pub. It was something to amuse and Mother would give us a few pennies to give him. One day in the summer we heard a strange sound coming from the direction of the Chapel. A few of us boys ran from the Cross and met the source of the music. A Scotsman, dressed in a kilt of a Highland Clan, was marching down the village street playing bagpipes. What a thrill that was. You see apart from Moody and Sankey at Chapel we were starved of music. We drank in the notes of the bagpipes. Never before had we heard such an instrument.

Every winter someone came from the British and Foreign Bible Society and gave a lantern lecture. Francis Cambridge and Cyril operated the lantern, a carbide or acetylene gas lamp which put a shadowy picture on the screen. Whether Cyril turned too much water on to the carbide one dark winter night or not I don't know, but the lamp set on fire. It was rather a pity, but fun for the half dozen boys who were warming themselves by the stove in the hall.

Normally the pictures were of missionaries. The topless natives of some far-flung empire were not supposed to entertain, but we were amused. I remember the giraffe-necked women from Burma and the hymn which showed up spotted and lined on the screen, 'The Church's One Foundation'. This was instilled upon us as the Church and Chapel sat together on this occasion.

High up on the hill above The Cuckoo Pen Mr Clements kept a few store cattle on Holcombe Knapp. This field of maybe 20 acres sloped steeply down to the Primrose Coppice while at the top an old quarry used to supply stone for the village roads. The feature peculiar to Holcombe Knapp was the long wiry grass which was spurned by both cattle and sheep. In winter when grass keep was short the cattle did tear some of the less wiry herbage.

Hugh Clements welcomed boys and girls on his field as a holiday playground. He provided staves from his cider barrels and the bigger boys constructed sledges. These rough-made vehicles glided down Holcombe Knapp as if the surface was snow covered. For hours we trekked up that slope and came down on the sledges at quite a pace. The wiry grass was described by Jubilee as being 'slick'. On hot summer afternoons it made popping noises like the bursting of the nearby gorse pods. When the March winds dried the grass its ripples were like the little waves of the sea, but not blue or green but khaki-coloured. No doubt artificial ski slopes are expensive to construct but here on Holcombe Knapp the boys and girls of The Cuckoo Pen enjoyed something for free.

I often think that we boys of the twenties had more fun playing conkers than those of today with their expensive and complicated computer games. A metal skewer from the butchers was an ideal tool for boring the hole in the fruit of the horse chestnut tree. The rules were simple, and when the conkers were baked a while in the oven their life on the string was increased. The call among the boys was 'Hobbledy hobbledy honker, my first conker'. Then the fun began. We kept a careful count of how many times our conker knocked out those of our opponents by dislodging them from their string.

A favourite game which could be noisy on winter evenings was Tipit, or Up Jenkins. Sitting on either side of the table one competitor held a three-penny joey or a little silver three-penny bit in his clenched hand. Three on each side of the table was ideal. We called 'Up Jenkins' and the six clenched fists on the opposite side were held in the air. Then we cried 'Jenkins on the table', and the fists came down on to the table. In turn we guessed which fist contained the coin, and said 'Take that one away. Take that one away'. Then with one fist remaining on the table, we said 'Tip it'. If we were successful, it would be the one clutching the coin.

Games like this passed the time on those oil-lamp lit evenings before the wireless and television robbed us of thinking for ourselves.

Church, Chapel and Politics

SUNDAY MORNING

It was Sunday morning, the bells at the Church called the folk to worship at one end of the village. Joe, Lofty and the Chapel folk with Flora, Cissy Tredwell from the post office and others, filled the pitch pine pews in the little Bethel up Blacksmith's Lane. The Church faithful made a procession down to the village Cross and the sixteenth-century Church. In their Sunday best they gave a picture of Conformity.

Mrs Pride, bursting from her shot-silk two piece, all navy blue and lace, marched rather than walked down the footpath followed by little Teddy Price in black with a shallow bowler hat, walking in tandem with his wife. We know that Teddy had been up early cleaning and dusting the panelled living-room at The Orchards. Last night he had picked the peas, and dug the new potatoes. But he accepted Petticoat Government; it gave him a sense of security.

Harry drove the pony and trap from the farm to the Church gates with his employer Mr Dunn and his good wife. Mr Dunn was one of the churchwardens. Blenheim, with Whistler, Stodge and Ponto sat at the back of the chancel. Cyril, brother-in-law to Revd Vernon and caretaker of the churchyard, was also a churchwarden. He sat with his staff with the copper head near the front of the Church.

Snob came from his Yew Tree Cottage, upright as a dart at seventy-three, an old soldier of the Boer War. He sat opposite Olive, the Merry Widow from Apple Acre. He was an agnostic but thought it was wise to keep an eye on that desirable lady. Only days before, when Olive had been entertaining none other than Sam, the paddle-steamer owner from town, Snob had called from the road outside Apple Acre to Olive in her bedroom. 'Olive, I hate you. If I'd got a gun I'd shoot you.'

Such was the competition for the hand of this village beauty.

Last of all the worshippers that Sunday was Dr Edward Overthrow. He was always late. Milly Bostock struck up the organ with Old Jubilee pumping away, sitting alongside Stocky, the clerk, whose Amens and responses added something extra to Revd Vernon's prayers. Stocky walked with his game leg to his place at the lectern, a man who seemed ageless, as if he had always been Clerk at St Luke's.

Service over, Stocky collected the prayer books and then performed his 'pièce de resistance' – those great puffs from that little corduroyed man as he blew out one candle after another.

THE MOTHERS' UNION

The Mothers' Union was a force to be reckoned with in the village. It was presided over by Miss Jeffreys, who was popular with a section of the 'Holier than Thou' folk of The Cuckoo Pen, and who divided her time between the union and the RSPCA.

Every year, one of Miss Jeffreys' tasks was to organize the annual cream tea, or bunfight. Poor Flora would have to miss out this year as she had been excommunicated from the union. Other members might have stood by her, but none of the mothers could afford to upset Miss Jeffreys, or miss the tea and cream cakes.

The tea was a grand affair. There was no piped water in the schoolroom, so Teddy Pride carried bucket loads from a standpipe for the tea-making and washing-up. Mrs Pride was the secretary, again like on Sundays all shot-silk and lace. It was very respectable. Chocolate éclairs and cream cakes followed the ham tea.

The invited speaker was a bachelor vicar from a neighbouring parish, Revd Brown. His pony was stabled at Teddy Pride's. What a smart turnout Revd Brown travelled in! A jet black cob with silver-mounted harness pulled the governess car, a rubber-tyred vehicle which hardly made a sound as the Parson's cob trotted up the village street.

Afterwards Revd Brown was caught in conversation with Miss Jeffreys. 'I've been invited by Revd Vernon to preach at St Luke's on Sunday week,' he said with a note of jubilation in his voice.

'Oh, come to tea, Alec may I call you? Alec, we have known each other for a while.'

'Yes, that is good,' came the reply.

Miss Jeffreys had also invited Becky, a widow, to her cottage for tea. What a mistake! Alec Brown ignored Miss Jeffreys over the meal. He found Becky, a quite eccentric young woman who had travelled widely in the Forces, very interesting. By the time the trifles were finished and the cake cut, Miss Jeffreys was boiling. All in a flap, she threw a cup of tea over Becky. The party was over but Alec had to get himself organized to preach at St Luke's. The two ladies sat either side of the font and delighted in Alec. He must have had something.

THE PARISH MEETING

From time immemorial villages were ruled by the 'vestry meeting', usually chaired by the Parson and the churchwardens, the way wardens and all the other appointed folk were there along with the rate payers, a few farmers, and so on. But all this changed in the 1880s when Parish Councils were introduced – either five or seven men or women elected to deal with parish affairs.

Stocky, the clerk, who said the Amens in St Luke's Church and supervised Sacco when he dug a grave, remembered the vestry meetings when his father was clerk. Things were passed then, he said, that were anything but honest. For instance the Parson, who elected his own churchwarden, also elected the people's warden. Tustin, the coalman, remembered that, and the fact that vestry meetings were always held at times when the working man couldn't attend. So the vestry meeting was abolished, to be replaced by the Parish Council.

There were so few rate payers in that time that those who claimed parish relief had to be satisfied with half a crown a week. The Squire employed men who walked on two sticks, saying, 'I have had the best out of you, now I'm having the worst.' If they went on 'The Parish' he, as the biggest rate payer, payed them for doing nothing.

Five men on the Parish Council held sway, but once a year the annual parish meeting was held. All rate payers were eligible to attend. These annual parish meetings used to be well attended and could be lively affairs. In later years Tom Dunn, who served on the District Council and also the Parish Council, came under fire from some of the better-off villagers. Because pressure in the old main was not enough, these folk wanted piped water to their half of the village. (The other half already had a private supply.) This would involve building a new water main to that area, which included the council houses. In turn this would increase the council house tenants' rent and rates from six shillings to twelve shillings a week. Tom Dunn maintained that the working man on thirty shillings a week could not afford extra rent and rates. Time passed and young Tom Dunn eventually became Chairman of the Parish Council. He was pretty good at assessing what questions would be asked at the annual meeting and would be ready with answers.

The new district councillor was a retired bank manager from Liverpool. He had become churchwarden and started an amateur dramatic society in The Cuckoo Pen. A good-looking man who had his hair waved, he walked the village with a fancy stick, trying all the time to look and act like one of the natives. No one like Eustace Shufflebottom had ever come to The Cuckoo Pen. Folk flocked from the neighbouring villages just to hear him read the lesson in Church. If it was Belshazzar's Feast, one could see the writing on the wall.

Women drooled over their morning coffee when Eustace was around. He took great exception to Frank Bird and the Plough and Harrow but was very much into cocktail parties with the upper crust.

In the first place Eustace had deposed George Hinton, a farmer whose family had farmed the Vale land since the time of the Commonwealth. He was a true countryman who would always help out. It once happened that the cricket club needed a new ground. The ground chosen was landed up, uneven, and badly drained. George's caterpillar tractor made the field suitable for sowing with grass seed and a good pitch was the result. George refused any payment, saying it was his effort towards the club. But then Eustace, supported by the gullible, beat George at the election and The Cuckoo Pen lost a benefactor.

When election time came around again Shufflebottom was opposed by a young farmer, who was narrowly defeated. The turnout was 94 per cent and Eustace won by ten votes. I suppose it's natural for folk to have doubts about people from outside, incomers or townees, especially when questions are raised about local issues. In Eustace's case it was about pollution in the brook, and unfortunately Eustace could only reply, 'Where is this brook?' At this, Jubilee, Frank Bird, Snob, and the rest had raised their eyebrows and persuaded the young farmer to stand.

It is true Eustace had a good brain but not when rural things were discussed. He was a product of the Mersey and the bank. To be fair though, he was a good amateur actor with a pleasing voice, which turned the ladies on and so they voted for him.

Becky, a regular attender at parish meetings had an old aunt who lived at Rose Cottage. She was fond of old Alice, who had played the Chapel organ since she was twelve and was now in her eighties. Becky came to the meeting, ready with her speech, the same one as last year, but nothing had been done.

'Mr Chairman,' she addressed young Tom Dunn. 'Mr Chairman, what about that manhole cover along Pig Lane in front of Auntie Alice's cottage? It's dangerous and if Auntie Alice was to catch her foot in it one dark night and break her leg who is going to pay?'

Tom Dunn turned to Eustace. 'That's your province, Mr Shufflebottom. The roads are no longer cared for by the Parish Council.'

Eustace stood at the little table in the schoolroom. Women took deep breaths. He was immaculate, his made-to-measure suit, his powdered, well-shaved face. He jingled some coins in his pocket and summed up the situation.

'Becky, you are right, that manhole is dangerous but Pig Lane is an unadopted lane. The Council are not responsible but as a favour to the parish the surveyor will send a man out immediately and make the manhole safe.'

The amazing thing about village life is how gullible folk are when a newcomer puts on the charm, has a pleasing accent, is handsome and smartly dressed. Eustace Shufflebottom was all these things.

Jubilee said, 'Whatever Eustace has in college education he's not one of us.'

'Why?' I questioned.

'First of all,' Jubilee continued, 'what about what happened last spring. There's an overhang over the eaves of his house. Tis here the house martins make their nests. Eustace with a long pole knocked down them houses of clay. I know they make a mess but live and let live I say.'

There was quite a wide grass verge outside Eustace's garden wall, Council ground but Eustace kept it mowed. When cows were driven along the village street they didn't like the hard road and chose to walk on the grass. Eustace was quite irate about this and grumbled to the farmers, but really anything outside the garden was planted at the owner's risk. A flock of sheep once cleared up a border of nasturtiums planted outside a garden wall. The two men in charge hadn't a chance to keep the animals from this salad. Some say that if you want to find an idiot in the country you have to take him there. Eustace was no idiot, but left it rather late in life to learn country ways.

But we must press on with the events at the parish meeting. Old Jubilee, the village oracle, knew every path and tree in the village.

He had been a collector of taxes and served at one time on the Parish Council and he was always at the parish meeting. He made cider from the old varieties of cider apples, strong stuff which affected the farm chaps in one of two ways. Some it made what they called benevolent, while others turned argumentative, wanting to fight. Jubilee had a thatched cottage where barrels of what was called Agricultural Brandy were stored.

'Mr Chairman,' he addressed young Tom Dunn, 'that hedge overgrowing the footpath and the lane down what we call Bachelor's Avenue is got so bad it scratches Mr Buchannan's buzz as he comes down from his garage.'

Mr George Buchannan had recently begun a bus service into the market town with a bus he had built in a bedroom of his house.

Tom Dunn replied, 'That hedge I believe belongs to Mrs Olive Beckford. The Clerk will remind her that the hedge needs cutting back. I'm sure Mr Buchannan's Brown Eagle bus should not be scratched by that hedge.'

Cyril got to his feet, saying, 'Is it necessary to write to Olive Beckford, her man Snob is here. He can give the message.'

It being pension day, Snob was well primed with Frank Bird's beer. His face flushed, he thumped the desk in front of him and roared at Cyril, 'You have not been in the village, Cyril, long enough to get your seat warm, so shut up. You are jealous of me. I know your pranks, sending bottles of wine at Christmas to Mrs Beckford. If I find you around her house I'll kick your ass.'

Stocky said, 'Now look yer you two men, that's enough.'

'And who are you to talk?' Snob added, then let out a great stream of bad language and abuse and left the schoolroom before he was asked to do so.

'Any more business?' Tom Dunn said and up jumped Teddy Pride, prompted by his gorgeous wife.

'Mr Chairman, I've noticed that now we have large buses coming to the village to collect the school children it is so dangerous along that narrow path when pensioners go to the post office. Can we have a wider footpath?'

Tom Dunn replied, 'That's all very well, Mr Pride, but if we do that makes the road even narrower for the buses.'

Tustin sucked his breath between his ill-fitting yellow false teeth and blurted out, 'Make the path wider by taking some land off folks' gardens. Them up by the post office, their gardens be more valuable to the shooting rights, thistles, docks and brambles.'

'Are you criticizing my garden, Tustin? Because if you are you can come and mow it for me,' Becky's words to the coalman put him in his place.

'Any other business?' Tom said again. 'The time is getting on and we aim to finish the meeting in an hour. Yes, Miss Jeffreys.'

'Mr Dunn, the path to the station has an overgrown hedge and it's impossible to walk along it for brambles.'

Tom Dunn was well aware of the state of the hedge along Station Road and had thought that the matter would be raised. He knew that the field was owned by Frank Bird. That morning Tom had rung Mr Bird who stated that he had no time to cut the hedge and could Tom have it cut and send him the bill. That afternoon Dunn's tractor driver with a hedge cutter had trimmed the hedge and cleared up the croppings.

'Have you been down the Station Road today Miss Jeffreys?' Tom enquired.

'No, not today Mr Chairman.'

'Well, I am assured that you will find Mr Bird's hedge has been cropped.'

With that, another parish meeting ended, and village politics went through the usual motions. The parish meeting had little power over the Parish Council. It's been said that the Parish Council is like a calf with its legs tied; it can bawl and do little else, but it is very important that the views of the local folk are heard.

THE GENERAL ELECTION

Elections in the twenties were a very regional affair. Candidates had to travel around the constituency and proclaim their policy. One such election which took place at The Cuckoo Pen is memorable.

Sir Thomas Davies had represented the area which included The Cuckoo Pen since the end of the First World War. A Conservative, of course. The farmers voted for him and persuaded their employees to do the same. The farmers said that Sir Thomas represented the area well. But Old Jubilee disagreed; he said the only time Sir Thomas opened his mouth in Parliament was to ask if someone could shut the window as he was in a bit of a draught. And it was Sapper's notion that if the biggest rogue in the country put up as a Conservative he would get in.

Agents of the parties came round and decided on headquarters, or a committee room, in a cottage. This was where the 'power house' would be. The Labour candidate's agent offered Tustin five shillings for the use of his front room on election day. The Conservatives were happy to have Stocky the parish clerk's thatched cottage at their disposal. The Liberals as far as I know had no committee room.

Tom Dunn, Revd Vernon, Teddy Pride, Dr Overthrow, Cyril and others all supported Sir Thomas. William Penny, Cissy Tredwell, Joe and Lofty were Liberals. The few Labour supporters were, in the main, Sapper, Snob, Tustin, Sacco, Whistler, Caleb and Pedlar. (Pedlar, an extremist who supported Communism, gave a bad name to the Labour party. He treated Snob and Aaron at the Plough and Harrow; bought Aaron a gramophone record of 'The Red Flag' which they sang at Tustin's house.) Frank Bird, the landlord of the Plough and Harrow, remained neutral; his customers came from all parties. Cissy Tredwell at the post office had the election manifestos to deliver, all full of promises, promises.

Some weeks before the date of the poll Sir Thomas came to The Cuckoo Pen. He was supported by a bunch of dyed in the wool

Tories from Cheltenham. They brought with them a comedian to draw the voters to the schoolroom. It worked; the school was packed for his meeting. Dr Overthrow took the Chair. Sir Thomas, an amiable looking man, stood at the schoolteacher's desk. Dressed in a black coat, pin-stripe trousers and wearing a huge blue rosette in his buttonhole, he looked the part. Miss Jeffreys sitting in one of the front desks drank in every word, giving little claps and whispering 'Hear, Hear'. Sir Thomas certainly went down well with The Cuckoo Pen Tories.

Snob and Tustin's brother Aaron had been to the Plough and Harrow. It was Snob's army pension day, and Frank Bird's beer had loosened their tongues as Snob proved when he challenged Sir Thomas. 'What have you lot done for we Old Soldiers who fought for you in the '14 war? Don't you see them walking the turnpike road?'

Sir Thomas was at a loss to answer. Snob had been a sergeant major during the First World War, after serving in the Boer War.

'Order,' Teddy Pride called from where he stood by the door.

Now Tustin and Aaron had lived through many elections. They never reckoned it a real contest without some fighting up and down the village street. Snob took the initiative, walking towards Teddy Pride with fists raised saying, 'Come on then, you yellow belly who dodged the column.'

PC Smith then escorted the two men from the school. Sir Thomas continued his talk.

Primed with the beer, Snob and Aaron left the cottage bent on mischief. Aaron offered to fight anyone who said they were voting Tory, and reckoned that every election in the village should be settled this way. In the moonlight of that May evening Aaron and Snob unhung the garden gates of all the Tory supporters. Dr Overthrow, Revd Vernon, Cyril, Miss Jeffreys and Teddy Pride. Mr and Mrs Pride's gate was propped against the post when the lady herself pushed it open and fell in the path. Dr Overthrow was called and he informed PC Smith. Nothing was proved, but everyone knew the culprits.

Meanwhile, after a break for coffee and biscuits, the Tory meeting continued and Cecil Bode, the Cheltenham comedian, did his part. Cecil did tricks with cards, took rabbits from hats and in all got the natives of The Cuckoo Pen wanting more. He then mixed with the folk where he chatted among the school desks. One middle-aged lady sat with her two young daughters. 'What's your name, Darling?' Cecil said to the younger daughter.

She answered, 'Grace.'

'It's Grace is it?' he replied, pondered a few seconds, then said, 'Grace, Disgrace and Candle Grace.' Not very complimentary names for the lady and her daughters.

A rather unkind titter went round the schoolroom, for the elder daughter he called Disgrace was a free spirit who believed in 'Free Love'.

Cissy Tredwell and her mother were strong Liberals but came to the meeting to hear Sir Thomas. Mrs Tredwell considered herself as pure as the driven snow. No bad language or anything she called 'suggestive' occurred in her post office. Cissy was kept on a tight rein. No one in the village was considered good enough to marry her, the daughter of an ex-schoolmistress.

Cecil Bode reeled off a string of tales to whet the appetite of all parties present. He was talking to farmers and farm workers. One tale went like this. Master Brown and his farm boy Jimmy were taking a load of hay up the lane when the load turned over. Jimmy ran to Master Jones' farm and asked for his help.

'Have a drink of cider, Boy. I know Master Brown, we are friends.'

Jimmy drank the cider. Master Jones then said, 'Here's some bread and cheese.'

Jimmy, all agitated, replied, 'Master Brown won't like me staying here.'

'What's the hurry, Boy?'

'Hurry, Master Jones? Master Brown is under that load of hay.'

Cecil Bode spoke of a farmer in the next village who employed a boy living in the house. This boy ran away, and came to Mr Jones' asking for a job.

'Why are you leaving? I know your employer.'

'Tis the vittle [food] Sir.'

'Now I know you would have good food on that farm.'

The boy replied: 'Well, the old cow died and we ate her. The old sow died and we ate her. Now the old woman has died. I thought it was time to leave.'

Mrs Tredwell was not amused but old men, young men and women roared with laughter. Cecil told of a party from Cheltenham going for a day trip on a charabanc to Weston-super-Mare. They saw a bus about to leave the sea front. One fellow asked the driver where he was going.

'I'm going to Burnham,' he replied.

The fellow, who had been drinking heavily, blurted out, 'I wish you could take my missus.'

But Cecil had a local story to tell concerning Sir Thomas Davies. No doubt the same tale had gone round all the villages in the constituency. A woman from Tewkesbury on the edge of Sir Thomas' constituency was keen on promoting the Conservative cause. There was only one party in her book. The local agent had some placards printed in large blue letters, TOM DAVIES AGAIN. The woman had twin boys about three months old and of course a twin pram. Not to be outdone she stuck a poster on her pram, TOM DAVIES AGAIN.

As the clapping died down Mrs Tredwell and Cissy, with their heads high in the air, walked from the schoolroom. Mrs Tredwell was heard to say as Teddy Pride opened the door for her to leave 'Suggestive'.

The meeting ended with the usual singing of 'God Save the King'. Everyone stood up bar Pedlar, who had no time for Royalty.

Political meetings by the other two parties were mere bagatelle compared with the kind Sir Thomas held. Tom Robbins, the Labour party candidate, spoke in the school to a fair audience with Pedlar in the Chair. It must be said that there was some noisy barracking from some of the Tories. PC Smith who had turned out Snob and Aaron from the Conservative meeting ignored this.

The Liberals held an open-air meeting one evening by the fifteenth-century village Cross. The candidate's name escapes me, but the main speaker was a farmer from a nearby village. A bearded Methodist local preacher, who I had been rook shooting with a couple of days before. William Penny, a lifelong Liberal, asked the candidate questions which they had agreed upon beforehand. Staged if you like, but it worked.

Dr Overthrow stated to the meeting that it was Lloyd George who let the farmers down after the war. He had promised to support them, then reneged on the corn prices and that's why the wages of the farm workers were cut in 1922. Could they be trusted again? The Liberals did have a fair meeting. They were tolerated in the village, whereas socialists were branded as being atheists and not loyal to the Crown.

The election was held in May, in perfect spring weather, and Sir Thomas Davies was returned as Conservative candidate. The Liberals put up a good show and came second. They had no doubt benefited by what had happened in a nearby village.

The gardener at The Court had taken the Chair at a Liberal meeting. The Squire there sacked him for not supporting the Conservatives. Being out of work, the Liberal Association bought him a horse and cart and he started a coal round. Acts like that of the Squire did no good to the Conservative cause. Tom Robbins just managed not to lose his deposit.

A pretty lively crowd gathered outside the school to hear the result of the poll. Aaron was there, in fighting mood. A few of the young Conservative supporters sang 'The Birds of the Air Fell Asighing and Asobbing When They Heard of the Death of Poor Cock Robin'. Tom Robbins, so sarcastically spoken of, had no chance. The folk of The Cuckoo Pen considered socialists traitors to what can be described as the status quo. The class system was to remain.

Pedlar was disappointed by the result of the election. He had never expected the socialists to win, but to be beaten by the Liberals and

William Penny was a hard pill to swallow. He was running his Model T Ford car as a taxi but few folk of The Cuckoo Pen patronized him. People farther afield did use him for trips to town and to Birmingham. But Pedlar had a cough. Some said he was consumptive. Miss Jeffreys, who had nursed in London, told Bunch at the Mothers' Union that his cough sounded like a smoker's cough. There was no sympathy for Pedlar among the middle class. Cyril said that a chain smoker of Woodbine cigarettes was asking for trouble.

Doctor Overthrow treated Pedlar and sent him to a specialist. The Doctor was a good friend of the Radical Labour. He was big enough to see Pedlar's point of view. The Doctor was a pale blue Tory. Miss Jeffreys, Bunch, Cyril and Mrs Pride were hoping that Pedlar would die, although Miss Jeffreys' professional prediction was that he may last some years.

When Pedlar did die The Cuckoo Pen lost the first of the true Radical Socialists, in fact a Communist, had there been such a candidate.

A problem arose at Pedlar's funeral. His house, garden and cherry orchard were up on the hill near the circle of trees known as The Cuckoo Pen. Pedlar had been used to creating a footpath unofficially through Tom Dunn's field and farmyard, and it was proposed to bring Pedlar in his coffin that way to the churchyard. But carrying a corpse through a field constituted making a right of way, and Tom Dunn was worried. He and Pedlar had always been good friends, but he couldn't allow the coffin to come through his field. The bearers went the long way round along a bridle road into a lane then down the village street. The working men followed, but little was said in the churchyard. Pedlar didn't believe in God. Sapper, with granite chippings, made a gravestone engraved with Pedlar's name and age. A tidy mark of respect for the man who caused such embarrassment to those in The Cuckoo Pen who were furious that there were Socialists there at all. Liberals could be tolerated but not Pedlar's party.

Round and About

GINGER BEER AND BRAWN

Two women lived at opposite ends of the village. The first one, Aunt Phoebe, made and sold ginger pop from an old recipe. She lived at the bottom of the village in a thatched cottage opposite the fifteenth-century Cross. Shoppy Bradfield, the Brawn Queen, occupied her own Victorian cottage with an apple orchard just past the Chapel at the top end of The Cuckoo Pen. Both were widows and both strong Chapel.

Phoebe, apart from making pop, had a little shop in her front room and sold sweets, chocolates, etc. She was a big woman, what her brother-in-law Jack called 'a boiling piece'. Jack lived with Phoebe and was known as a rough carpenter, mending farm implements and gates. He was a cunning rabbit catcher, who had an Irish terrier whose name was Rough. Jack had drinking sessions which could go on for a couple of weeks. Phoebe used to remonstrate with him, but to no avail. The sessions were always the result of some argument.

Jack was a nice old boy who always started his drinking at the Plough and Harrow with a quart pot which Frank Bird kept for him. One hears that when Jack had had one or two pints he would say, 'Them two mugs on the shelf be just alike, especially that one.' And of course when one of Frank Bird's customers said that they could see a fly on Broadway Tower 6 miles away Jack replied, 'I've just seen him wink his eye.'

A friend of Jack's, known as Walt, used to lodge at Aunt Phoebe's. When they came home drunk they had difficulty in climbing the stairs. Taking it in turns the two men made a run from the wash-house door to the staircase in the living-room. After several attempts they reached their bedroom.

When not drinking beer Jack took a bottle of Aunt Phoebe's pop with him to work. Mind you, when Phoebe's pop had been kept for a fortnight it was more lethal than the cider from the Plough and Harrow, and Phoebe was supposed to be teetotal!

In her kitchen this ginger beer was rightly called pop, for corks flew and bottles exploded when the brew had matured for a while. The corks were normally tied down with pudding string.

Where Phoebe got her bottles from is a mystery. They were all shapes and sizes but mostly Camp Coffee bottles. The larger sizes which held a pint and a half cost two-pence while the smaller ones were a penny halfpenny. Folks were pretty good to old Phoebe, taking back the empties, although some were still found under the hedges in the hayfields. Apart from pop, Aunt Phoebe made raspberry vinegar and peppermint essence. Jack gathered a kind of peppermint known as parmint off the duck pond at The Manor.

For Phoebe's own consumption a relative of hers from the Black Country introduced her to bee wine. The so-called bees in a glass jar were fed with sugar. Quite non-alcoholic, or was it? I've seen red faces and heard loosened tongues from the drinkers of bee wine.

Phoebe spoke quite often of her family, how she was the middle child of a family of eleven. One of her elder sisters went into domestic service in Nottinghamshire and when Phoebe went there on a weekend visit they went to Chapel. Back home she told her mother and father of a peculiar hymn they sang: 'Jesus of Nazareth parsnip wine'. That was how it sounded to young Phoebe. The hymn of course was their dialect for 'Jesus of Nazareth passeth by'.

Shoppy Bradfield was not one of the local folk. She had come with her late husband from London. He was keeper to the Squire when he had to be looked after. As Old Jubilee put it, 'The Squire went off his yud'.

Shoppy had a shop, but her main source of income was the eggs from her hens in the orchard and the production of brawn. Hence she became known as the Brawn Queen. Jarvie the pig killer kept Shoppy supplied with pigs' heads, pigs' faces, for her to manufacture the brawn.

The basins of Shoppy's efforts, which could not really be called a delicacy, found their way into the homes and the fields of the working men. Like Phoebe's pop bottles Shoppy's basins sometimes finished up under the hedges of the hayfields too.

The sale of the brawn helped to provide the money needed to build the new Chapel. Joe, Lofty and Shoppy worked together to raise money in all sorts of ways. However, Joe did fall out with the Brawn Queen once, over a basin he took with him to the smallholding. He said that just above where the brawn came up to in the basin was a rim of rice pudding. That put Joe off brawn for ever.

Every Saturday morning Shoppy Bradfield limped her way to the railway station. A bad hip which could not be replaced in the 1920s gave her that particular walk. She pushed her high pram called a bassinet loaded with her eggs, dressed chickens and brawn. The pram was handy for Shoppy because it could be loaded into the guard's van of the train, and then she would push it through the town to the market place. Some called her Mrs Egg Bradfield and her big brown eyes were reminiscent of eggs.

In town she met one of the elders of the village Chapel. The elder was manager of a large store, and had ideas about raising money for the new Chapel. Shoppy combed the second-hand shops for clothes, and brought back a pram load to sell to the villagers. The profit went to the Chapel. Then she organized draws, raffles, etc. which rather put the backs up of Joe and Lofty, who recognized this as the thin end of the wedge for gambling.

The Brawn Queen was a woman for her time, and it was a time when money was scarce. Her second-hand clothes and her brawn were a Godsend to the thirty-shillings-a-week labourers of the land.

THE BROWN EAGLE

In the 1920s the folk who lived around The Cuckoo Pen were quite privileged as far as public transport was concerned as the loop line on the railway was a good connection to town. The young folk of the time were addicted to the cinema, and they would regularly catch the train into town. Indeed, the pictures on a Saturday night were a must for the courting couples of The Cuckoo Pen. The problem was the last film didn't end until 10 o'clock, and the last train to the villages departed at 9 o'clock.

George Buchannan sought a remedy to the situation. George was a relative of Kenneth Horne of Moreton-in-Marsh, and he married Mr Penny's daughter just after the First World War. He had worked in munitions and had piloted the steamer *Lillybird* up and down the Avon. He was a born mechanic, and aimed at providing a bus service for the villagers.

The Brown Eagle coach, built on a Guy chassis, made the headlines in the local paper. GEORGE BUCHANNAN BUILDS THE BROWN EAGLE IN A BEDROOM read the headlines, and it was true. This twenty-seater bus was built by George in a bedroom.

George could see the needs of late Saturday night shoppers and the cinema goers and ran his last bus from outside the cinema at 10 o'clock. Shops and hairdressers were all open till that late hour in the twenties. Now, it usually happens that when a man starts a service of any kind, the big firms object. The traffic commissioners and the Midland Bus Company tried their best to get George off the road. But George canvassed the villagers for support – and won the day.

The Buchannans were a talented couple, George the mechanic and Anne his wife, deft with needle and thread. In the 1920s when fashions seemed unimaginative Anne provided some creations worthy of The Promenade shops of Cheltenham. She made my first sailor suit but that's what's known as a mere bagatelle.

Their sixteenth-century house at the top of what was jokingly known as Bachelor's Avenue was surrounded by a beautiful garden, the work of Anne. The furniture in the house was all in keeping with the period and was supplemented by George's work in his carpenter's shop. What intrigued me as a child was the fireplace. A little brass tap at the opposite side to the oven gave hot water; it seemed like magic in those days. While George built his bus Anne had upholstered the seats and made the curtains.

There was no need to buy a local newspaper, everything was discussed and argued about en route to town. Market gardeners bragged about crops, and the niceties and otherwise of family life were delved into. The journey home on those Saturday nights was the source of all the news and the gossip of the village.

Some shoppers put their baskets on the seats they wished to reserve and that could cause trouble. One Saturday night Flora had put her basket on a seat at the back of the bus. Stodge removed it and took the seat. When Flora returned she told Stodge that she had reserved the seat, only to get the reply, 'I be one of Mr Buchannan's most regular customers and I beunt moving for nobody.'

The seat immediately behind George was that of Becky, who was one of the many who fancied him. For Flora to take that seat would be as bad as sitting in the churchwarden's pew at St Luke's. That seat was for Becky, and George enjoyed her backchat. All the passengers liked George and always backed his driving. 'He never gi'n you much room, Mr Buchanan,' they would remark after a close shave.

George would reply, 'He never gave me any room at all.'

On those Saturday nights some passengers stayed for an extra pint at the Rose and Crown across the road. They hindered the Brown Eagle's departure from outside the Scala (pronounced Scaila by the locals).

Amy was often guilty of holding up the bus. The passengers who wanted to get home spoke disparagingly of her. Flora, her mother, with her black neckband and Olive's cast-off fur coat, said nothing. Tustin ventured the remark, 'I specs her got a bloke or two to see.' At maybe 10.30 the Brown Eagle left High Street making for The Cuckoo Pen 6 miles away.

Buchannan left the village green every day at 2 o'clock. So, the bus company put on one of their buses at 2 o'clock on the main road. George was worried that they would pick up his passengers, and played a cat and mouse game with his opposition. In a carefully planned manoeuvre the Brown Eagle ignored one passenger at a stop in the next village. But George knew that four people would be waiting at the next stop and if he picked up the one passenger, the company bus behind him would take the four. It developed into a kind of race between the Brown Eagle and the bus company.

Sunday school trips to Weston-super-Mare became the in-thing at this time. The Brown Eagle provided transport. It is always difficult to get the numbers right on these outings. As a general rule, three children or two adults were allowed on each seat. It happened that one child too many came on one morning in summer, so George put a stool up the aisle of his bus to solve the problem. Unfortunately a police patrol noticed that the aisle was blocked, and pulled over the Brown Eagle. George's fine for overloading took his profit for the day.

When the war and petrol rationing put many cars off the road the Brown Eagle became a lifeline for villagers who wanted to go to town. The twenty-seater bus some Saturday nights had eighty passengers, and it would groan its way in third gear over the river bridge to town. Half the passengers got off at the Red Horse pub, and the overcrowded bus didn't look quite so bad in the middle of the town.

When George retired his bus was towed to Shoppy Bradfield's orchard and became a fowl house for some of her hens. The bus had been an institution and would be sorely missed.

THE DEER ESCAPE FROM THE PARK

The General had an estate adjoining The Cuckoo Pen which included a large area of parkland with a herd of deer. The deer had been there since the Middle Ages. The General's ancestors, all military men, had seen service in the British Army as far back as the Battle of Corunna.

Jarvie, the last of the General's gamekeepers, used to cull the deer with his rifle with a telescopic sight. He always shot an avian, a castrated stag two years old, for the feast at the Bell Ringers Supper. As the fawns were born in the thick bracken of the hill Jarvie castrated some of the males. He said they made better eating than the strong-tasting stags.

The fences around the park to enclose the deer were falling into disrepair; Jarvie and the General were getting too old to maintain them. Deer fences made of cleft oak eight or ten feet high were also difficult to obtain. One autumn the inevitable happened – the herd of deer escaped from the park and began to attack the crops of the farmers, market gardeners and smallholders like Joe and Lofty. As the hard winter weather came on fields of sprouts were devastated.

Jim Cambridge, whose land adjoined the General's, was friendly with his neighbour, in fact he often joined in the pheasant shoots at the park. Jim, an ironmaster from the Black Country, had over the years become a part of the scene at and around The Cuckoo Pen but he was concerned about the damage done by the deer, especially to Joe and Lofty's sprout crop.

Jim wrote to the General:

Dear Francis,

You are no doubt aware that the deer from your Park have broken the fence and are damaging crops on the hill. They belong to you and I would be obliged if you would instruct your men to drive them back into the Park.

Looking forward to hearing from you.

> Yours sincerely,
> Jim Cambridge.

On receipt of the letter the General was doubtful whether Jim Cambridge was serious about driving deer back to the park or whether he was leg-pulling. He called Jarvie and showed him what had come in the post.

Jarvie laughed, saying, 'I don't think he's serious, Sir.'

The General replied to Jim Cambridge and explained that all the men of the park and all the men of The Cuckoo Pen would not be able to drive the deer back on to his land. He added that if the deer damaged crops, you are at liberty to shoot them.

The villagers got pretty desperate at The Cuckoo Pen that autumn. As it was the rutting season, when the stags can be aggressive, some folk were wary when walking the footpaths, especially around Coney Burrows where Flora lived and where Lofty and Joe had their market garden.

On one occasion, at what the locals called the edge of night, Flora was taking in her washing from the line at Coney Burrows. Caleb, her man, was away in the Forest of Dean visiting his aged mother, leaving Flora alone apart from her children. From the cabbage patch past the clothes line Flora was startled by the rutting call of a stag, a heavy grunt. He and one of the does were feeding on the cabbage in the garden. Flora, petrified, ran with her washing into her cottage. After tea she took the children down the path to Lofty's cottage. She was in tears.

Over a cup of tea Flora, Lofty and Lofty's wife discussed what could be done about the deer. Lofty suggested a parish meeting which was agreed upon by the Parson, the Doctor and Jim Cambridge.

When Caleb returned from visiting his mother he was determined to have revenge on the deer for ruining his sprout crop and his spring cabbage. The animals had entered the garden through a hole in the hedge between two elderberry bushes. Now, that crafty blacksmith from the Forest of Dean had caught badgers on the hill with steel wire snares. (He cured the hams of Brock, salting them like he would pigs.) He had an idea. He fixed a steel wire snare between the elder bushes and anchored it to the stump of the elder, and waited.

It was the night of the full moon as Caleb sat under his apple tree, watching the place where the snare was set. He listened, the cock pheasant called from the wood beyond, disturbed on their perches in the larch trees. The deer came towards Caleb and Flora's garden. Flora sat at the bedroom window worried about her man. She listened to the call of the rutting stags. Caleb, out of sight by the apple tree, waited. One young doe poked its head through the gap in the hedge and into the snare. As the doe struggled, the snare tightened, and the rest of the herd ran across the hill. Caleb killed the doe with his butcher's knife and hammer. He dragged the carcase into the garden shed. He had some knowledge of butchering and took out the deer's liver and lights, then hung the carcase on a beam in his shed.

Flora woke next morning to the smell of something appetizing coming from the frying pan. Caleb was frying deer's liver for breakfast.

'Caleb,' she called from the bedroom, 'Caleb, are we having bacon for breakfast this morning? Did you bring some back from the Forest, home cured, from your Mother?'

Caleb smiled to himself then called back, 'Tis liver, Flora my old Butt, from that young deer. We be gwain to live like fighting cocks on venison.'

Flora came down to the kitchen. Caleb was already eating liver and dipping his bread in the frying pan. 'Yours is on the hob. I do look forward to you and the kids living on grub fit for the King.'

Over breakfast Caleb said that he was contacting Sacco at dinner time to ask him to come up and joint the venison.

'Sacco dos't know,' Caleb continued. 'Him didn't serve his apprentice next to old Fred Pope for nothing. He can butcher meat.'

Flora laughed, adding, 'Ah, and he can eat some. Half a dozen eggs fried is nothing to that plasterer.'

The fact that Caleb had snared the young doe didn't stop the rest of the deer ravaging crops around The Cuckoo Pen, but most of all on Joe and Lofty's holding at Coney Burrows.

It was an unofficial parish meeting at The Cuckoo Pen schoolroom, chaired by Dr Overthrow. Frank Bird proposed that a deer shoot be held on the following Saturday to reduce the damage done to crops on the hill, Joe and Lofty's in particular. He added that the shoot could only go ahead if Tom Dunn and Jim Cambridge agreed, because it was over their land that they would be shooting. Jubilee seconded the motion. All were in favour except Miss Jeffreys, Cyril and Jim Cambridge's son, Francis. Miss Jeffreys said that the shoot was barbaric and that it was up to farmers to fence against the deer.

A call was then made for volunteers to beat the wood and at this point Tustin rose to speak. 'I want to know, Mr Chairman, when the deer be shot who's going to have the venison? 'Cos the missus says that I can go beating only if we get our share of the venison.'

'Ah, Tustin! Thee bist the same old money grubber. I know thy Father gave thee a good hiding when thee was just a lad for giving something away. We ull give thee some meat Old Butt.'

The shoot on the following Saturday was something I'll never forget. The main guns were Dr Overthrow, with his precious Purdy twelve-bore; Milko, with a single-barrel converted rifle; Joe and Lofty, carrying their muzzle loaders; Frank Bird and his double-barrel hammer gun (he also brought two spaniel dogs with him); Laughing Tom, with a twelve-bore pin fire shot gun; and young Tom Dunn, who was proud of his eight-bore duck gun which his father had bought years ago in a sale. This long-barrelled firing piece kicked like a horse and the report from its huge cartridges echoed for miles.

Sacco organized the beaters under the direction of Laughing Tom. He had managed to enlist Caleb, Tustin, Ponto, Blenheim, Harry and Tat Steward.

The deer had been sighted that morning by Caleb up among the elder bushes on the edge of the wood. The beaters drove about a

A man of many parts. An old soldier, rabbit trapper and fast bowler in the cricket team

The parish meeting. Did we speak our minds tonight?

The Brown Eagle passing through the Avon floods

Ginger beer and brawn

Ploughing in progress with a four-horse team – the foreman, the body
horse, the lash horse and the filler

A threshing gang with steam engine. There were jobs for men, women
and children

Tustin sitting on the cover over the standpipe from where he carried his drinking water

Aaran outside his cottage. He could mow an acre of grass in a day, and on Election Day would fight with anyone who disagreed with him

An early combine harvester. Jack and I filled the sacks of corn

Off to town in a Sunbeam car

A soldier on leave, one of the Worcesters, with his parents

Peace celebrations with the carnival king and queen

dozen deer through the elder and across a ride in the wood where the motley assortment of guns stood. It was pretty disorganized. The men with twelve-bore, eight-bore, muzzle loaders, etc., stood in a semi-circle, alarmed at the sudden arrival of their prey.

This was a far cry from the pheasant shoots on an adjoining estate. What with the report of the guns and the smoke of the muzzle loaders lying as a smoke screen, it wouldn't have surprised me if there had been two-legged mortals among the bag! Bob Sandford and I ran behind the blackberry bushes away from the carnage. I had already experienced being shot through the ear by a trigger-happy crowd one Boxing Day years before.

One must bear in mind that all this happened sixty years ago, before common sense decreed that deer should only be shot with rifles. Young Tom Dunn killed the first deer with that eight-bore duck gun, two young stags followed, felled by Laughing Tom and Frank Bird. Four of the herd lay dead among the bracken, the rest of the deer made for the hill at the double. It's fair to say no animal was merely wounded, all those that were hit were killed.

There followed a trek down from Canks Bank through Tater Hill into Coney Burrows and down the lane to Laughing Tom's little farm, the deer carried on poles by the beaters. The guns were confronted in the lane by Jim Cambridge's son, who deplored the killing and told us so. Laughing Tom replied, 'That's all very well, Francis, but Joe and Lofty's greenstuff has been ruined.'

At Laughing Tom's farm he and Sacco hung the deer in the big wash-house to wait for the next morning when they were to be jointed. Oh, yes, Tustin had some meat, in fact, the whole of The Cuckoo Pen lived on venison for a while. The local policeman liked his venison high. It was high alright, he hung a haunch up in one of Laughing Tom's apple trees. As Tom said to Mella, he would cut a piece off when it was almost black.

From the day of the shoot the deer were culled, if that's the right term, because of the stealth of men like Frank Bird and Laughing Tom. But the herd multiplied and today it is a very healthy part of the fauna on the hill.

The deer did pose a problem for the local Hunt. Often the hounds chased the deer from covert to covert. A sight I recall is of a big almost black stag with a good head of antlers running in front of the hounds and jumping one of our five-barred gates as if it were nothing.

But that Saturday shoot stayed in our minds. It really was an amateur affair, and we were lucky that no one got injured.

Wartime and After

A VILLAGE AT WAR

From that fateful Sunday in September 1939, something happened to village life which is not easy to describe. The folk in The Cuckoo Pen had always been more or less independent of central authority. The Parish Council made recommendations to the District Council and the County Council. What The Cuckoo Pen wanted was usually granted. The rate of pay offered by Sir Robert McAlpine to those willing to help build the Army Camp tempted men to leave their work on the land. As unskilled labourers they were soon conscripted into the forces.

This resulted in a dearth of manpower in the fields of The Cuckoo Pen. The menfolk had to be replaced by Land Girls, Prisoners of War and Gang Labour supplied by the War Agricultural Committee. Within months The Cuckoo Pen was unrecognizable because of the influx of so many from the town and city.

Being 80 miles from the sea and very rural, the village was reckoned to be a safe place for about fifty evacuees from a Midland city. They came with their teachers to be absorbed by the cottage dwellers and the farmers' wives. Bus loads of parents came on Sundays to sit in Frank Bird's kitchen at the Plough and Harrow until 2 o'clock closing time. The dialect from a Midland city was quite different from the countryman's drawl. The children adapted themselves well away from the bright lights, the cinema, the trains, the fish and chip shops, city life. Pasty-faced boys and girls from the back streets grew fat and rosy-cheeked in the harvest fields and orchards of The Cuckoo Pen. Children who only knew milk from bottles drove the cows for milking to the farmyard. They scrumped the apples and plums, upsetting their tummies until they got used to so much fruit. Old Blenheim begged me not to let his two boys, Frank and Ernest, eat my pears. His words to me were, 'You know the Missus is fed up with them messing their trousers.'

Cottagers who had let their pigsties crumble, having bought cheap Danish bacon from town for years between the wars, now needed the sties. Some were refurbished and the folk without a sty built new ones in corrugated iron in their gardens.

A pig club was formed, and by surrendering bacon coupons balancer meal could be bought from the village baker. It was called balancer 'meal' but it did contain sawdust. All the waste from the kitchen, along with potatoes, parsnips, was put in a hogshead barrel called a swill tub. Even the washing-up water went in. How it stank, how it fermented, but the pigs thrived on the mixture.

The ways folk beat the rationing were amazing. Plums or pears were soaked in Campden Solution and then put into Kilner Jars and sweetened with saccharine. Runner beans were preserved in salt. Hedges were cleared of blackberries which were made into jam, using the small sugar ration. With no foreign apples being imported the English fruit was like gold. Every apple over one and a half inches in diameter could command the controlled price – never mind if it was as sour as a crab. Rabbits were a godsend too, in the days before myxomatosis. A meal for the countryman. It's true they did do damage to crops, but here was food for free.

The influx of what the locals called 'Townees', also brought benefits. Never had so many new members attended at Church and Chapel. The Land Girls provided partners for village youths at the occasional dance. A dance band from the next village gave a semblance of modern jazz. The girls were intrigued by these 'dos' in the army hut hall, where some of the old dears sat around and did their knitting. The girls billeted in the village fared better than those from the hostels, fed on Spam and processed cheese.

Things changed when the American soldiers came to a nearby army camp. Some Land Girls fell for the flannel of men – with the gift of the gab they spoke of their 'Estates' over the water, of going to the flicks and, after a few dances, about 'taking a breather, Honey'. With these last words couples would take to the night-time harvest and hayfields of The Cuckoo Pen.

When the American army came to Oakchurch Camp Colonel Franklin was their CO. A big Californian soldier, heavy with brass, Colonel Franklin had met Olive Beckford in the Plough at Cheltenham. It was not long before a Khaki Humber Snipe car was seen outside Olive's house at The Cuckoo Pen. The Colonel was having an affair with the luscious Mrs Beckford. Olive's lawn and shrubbery reached to the lane opposite Snob the cobbler's Yew Tree Cottage. To say that Snob was jealous is putting it mildly. He would sit up by his bedroom window watching Olive and the Colonel lovemaking under a weeping willow tree. Every detail of what went on under that tree Snob related to the customers at the Plough and Harrow. It's true Snob was only in the second division in Olive's book, after Dr Overthrow had warned him of his excesses, and that Sam from the nearby town had taken his place as the main visitor after the death of Norman. But what riled the shoemaker was how the Colonel showered presents on to his new love. Snob saw the great joints of beef from Oakchurch canteen carried from the car into Olive's house, then bottles of champagne, flowers and perfume.

Snob sighed over his pint at Bird's pub, saying, 'I know I can't compete with that sort of money, but it hurts my pride.'

The Colonel and Olive normally drank whisky at a hotel 2 miles away. Frank Bird didn't have a licence to sell spirits. However, Colonel Franklin took a liking to the cider at the Plough and Harrow and they began to use that pub for their refreshment instead.

When the couple arrived Snob, Blenheim, Harry, Sapper, Stocky and Caleb all gave them a wide berth. Now, at that time cigarettes were in short supply, in fact Frank Bird had only a meagre ration for his customers. Sapper filled his pipe with home-grown tobacco. He was generous to his friends. The Colonel and Olive arrived in the army car on to Frank Bird's gravel, outside where the sign of the Plough and Harrow squeaked in the wind. They came into the bar smoking Camel cigarettes. The smoke whetted the appetites of the tobacco-starved locals. 'Perhaps he will hand the packet round,' Blenheim said. 'That is, if he's a man.'

They watched from their bench by the door. The American and Olive sat in the chimney corner and when they had smoked half a cigarette they threw the half-smoked butt into the fire. After a few more sips at their cider they lit up two more cigarettes.

Caleb's words summed up what everyone was thinking. 'It's a pity we have had to bring in the Yanks. They was late a coming in to the '14 war. It's true they got the money but to me they be nothing but piss and wind.'

Caleb's comments brought a titter from his friends – all except Snob, that is. The ex-serviceman who had fought the Boers didn't share in the laughter.

One evening in the Plough and Harrow the Colonel and Olive were drinking their cider when a blonde girl with a lovely complexion and a figure which made the men look twice came through the door. It was Amy, the daughter of Flora from Coney Burrows. She was closely followed by Sacco, who bought her a shandy. The Colonel couldn't keep his eyes off this twenty-four-year-old bombshell. Olive was forty-eight!

Some nights later Snob at his bedroom window witnessed a flaming row between the Colonel and Olive. He was delighted. The Colonel apparently had been out with the beauty from Coney Burrows and the beef and champagne had been taken up there.

Poor Amy. She fell for his flannel and what's more he got her in the family way, then went with his section to France on D-Day, never to be heard of again. Amy's little boy Jim was a picture, and a comfort to Flora.

So the village girls fell for the men from overseas. Most kept out of trouble but Joe and Lofty did condemn the servicemen for their free lovemaking. They spoke to Miss Jeffreys, reporting their lack of morals, with no marriage vows. They told her, to her disgust, how the jackdaws were picking up their 'rubber goods' and dropping them from the hill on to their market garden.

'They be stamped with USA, Miss, there's no denying.'

A City Industrialist

Soon after the beginning of the war a farm with a Georgian farmhouse came on the market. Mr Charles Thomson, a Birmingham industrialist, bought the 250 acres, and a row of cottages on the hill just below The Cuckoo Pen which was on his land.

Charles, a man of about sixty, had ideas to improve life for all who lived at The Cuckoo Pen. He had influence with government departments which mattered, and was held in high regard for his involvement with the production of heavy machinery for the War Effort.

Charles did nothing by halves. He put a chap named John Brown in one of his houses as bailiff. Soon Wood Farm had all the modern implements of the day to work the land. When machinery was on quota, Mr Thomson got what he wanted. Two new tractors came from somewhere but his pride and joy were two Suffolk Punch horses. They were a picture on the Midland clay, where the heavy Shires had plodded over the land from time immemorial.

In the stable Charles looked at the harness, some of which was mended with string. 'This won't do, John. Pop down to Ernie the Saddler and order new gears for the horses. I've already asked him to make a new set of harness for Polly the pony, the one that pulls my governess car.'

We saw and admired Charles' cob trotting through the lanes of The Cuckoo Pen, and with its driver, very smart in a silver-grey suit and that Moss Bros trilby.

Mrs Thomson was, I'd say, younger than her husband. She looked a well-preserved fifty, with honey blonde hair. They made a picture in the governess car. She brought Pamela with her, her hairdresser from Birmingham. Pamela joined the Land Army and worked in the dairy.

Charles was in no way aping the Squire or the landed gentry. It is true that Charles and his good wife didn't suffer all the hardships of a rural lifestyle. They kept a Jersey cow, which provided cream for butter making – I doubt if they ever tasted margarine – and home-cured bacon and eggs laid in the orchard took the sting out of rationing. But Charles was a hard-headed business man, who helped the War Effort in the city and in the country.

John Brown, the bailiff, had been to university. What subjects he took is a mystery. He made many mistakes on the farm. Finding some seed in the tallet above the stable and believing it to be clover seed he planted Little Hill by the ring of beeches, grew a crop of lettuce! That got talked about in the Plough and Harrow. But mistakes like that were permissible in wartime when there's a market for most things.

This upright military-looking man, dressed to the nines in Bedford cord breeches, leggings and a hacking jacket, was a bit of a clown among the hobnailed farm workers. He drove a fast car and soon became a leading light at Farmers' Union meetings. Jonny, as he was known, employed four or five staid workers, poaching them from local farmers with offers of higher wages.

Charles, viewing the mixed herd of cattle he had taken at valuation from the previous owner of Wood Farm, scowled as he leant on the cowyard fence. 'Brown,' he called, 'I am ashamed of what I see here. This bunch of nondescript cattle – send the lot to market.'

But the Birmingham industrialist thought that his young bailiff was not up to buying some replacement Shorthorns. So he contacted a reputable dealer himself, who promised to send twenty roan heifers, pedigree Shorthorns. Similarly, he wouldn't allow the bailiff to go to the sheep sales on his own. 'You see, Brown,' he explained, 'when my friends come here from the city I want them to see some real quality stock. The sheep sales in the Border country are coming soon. You are to go with my friend the dealer and buy a flock of pedigree Kerry ewes.'

Things were looking up at Wood Farm. Tom, the young carter, ploughed the hill land with the two Suffolk horses, Punch and Jack. What a picture they made with their new harness and their shining liver chestnut coats.

Tom's wife Lynda had two young children. He was a good family man, but did spend too much time at the Plough and Harrow where he was the ace darts player in the pub team. A young Land Girl, Pamela, joined the team. She really fancied the young carter, and Tom was generous at the local hotel when the team played away. The gin and tonics brought the two closer together. Uninhibited, it was evident that the young married man and the Land Girl could have got involved.

Word got back to Lynda that Tom and Pamela were having an affair, but jealous tongues had exaggerated the facts. Even so, sparks flew at Tom's cottage below The Cuckoo Pen. But when Charles heard of the trouble and had words with his carter, and with Pamela, the flirtation died like a dream.

Bob Price was in charge of the ewes. They grazed Canks Bank, Holcombe Knapp and Furze Hill. Every morning Bob rode a Welsh cob around the flock, checking for maggots and foot rot, and then he fed the roan heifers on Little Hill. Bob was a good find for John Brown, he had experience with animals.

When the Shorthorn bull arrived from the sale at Reading, Charles and John Brown decided to turn him among the heifers in June so that they would calve the following March. A local vet persuaded John to have the heifers injected so that they came on bulling, or in season, during a short period. The disaster that followed on Little Hill had to be seen to be believed. Most of the twenty heifers were bulling the same day. The bull was helpless for as soon as he mounted one heifer another beast knocked him off. Heifers were riding the bull, heifers were riding each other. Eventually the poor bull, exhausted, failed to serve any of them. John brought him back to the yard and waited for the Shorthorns to come in season naturally.

The orchards at Wood Farm had been neglected. Trees had not been pruned, the wiry grass between the rows was spurned by the sheep. Charles bought a pitch-pole harrow to be pulled by the Fordson tractor to rip the grass from its roots. By constantly working up and down the orchards, then across, Bob Price created an arable field between the trees. Charles could get fertilizer when other farmers had to manage without. John and Bob sowed heavy dressings of complete fertilizer, what the locals called artificial, and then a dressing of sulphate of potash. The trees that had grown tall and ungainly were cut back to a reasonable height. Charles ordered John to see to that, for he said he was not going to risk the necks of his workers picking fruit from such a height. The following years trees which had been barren yielded the most saleable plums, apples and pears in the orchards of Wood Farm.

Old Jubilee reckoned he knew the names of the varieties of fruit on Wood Farm. There were so many sorts, some very old, some relatively new. One variety of pears I remember was Belle of Brussels, and apples like Drunken Willy come to mind. With notebook in hand Charles Thomson recorded the names as Jubilee related them to him. Next year when Charles asked Jubilee the name of apple, pear or plum he sometimes came out with a different one. Charles was amused; he had kept a record.

Everything was going well at The Cuckoo Pen. The Kerry ewes lambed 150 per cent on the hill. The roan Shorthorn cows were in milk. Charles sent John to the War Agricultural Committee Advisory Department to learn about growing linseed to balance the dairy rations. The staff under John, who was learning the art of farming, were happy, but when John tried dictator methods on the Italian prisoners they downed tools. 'You must humour them, Brown,' the boss insisted. 'That's how to get the best from them.'

Schemes were afoot to bring electricity to the old cottages on the hill and Charles had an idea for building a house just below the circle of trees. He got planning permission to erect a Cotswold stone house there. A bulldozer levelled an area of land which overlooked the Cotswold Hills. The Cuckoo Pen Squire from Birmingham was about to make a miniature garden city like Cadbury's had done in Bournville.

At a board meeting of his firm in Birmingham this good industrialist dropped dead with a heart attack. Many of the hopes and dreams of The Cuckoo Pen disappeared when he died, but while he lived in the village Charles Thomson made a mark which will never be forgotten.

THE DARKER SIDE OF
THE CUCKOO PEN

As life in the cities became difficult and dangerous because of enemy air raids during the Second World War, country villages became a sanctuary, a refuge. The folk who came were in the main good, honest people who made a valuable contribution to a restricted, blacked-out world. A few took advantage of trusting, simple country folk. One such person was a hard-headed business man.

Mr Bryant, a retired captain of industry from the Midlands, had been used to employing hundreds of workers in his factory. He bought two semi-detached cottages from me. His son-in-law, an architect of some standing, converted the cottages into one house by taking down the middle chimney. Mr and Mrs Bryant made efforts to become integrated (if that is the word) into village life. He was a supporter of the cricket team, his wife the WI and the Church.

The Cuckoo Pen folk on the whole were delighted, for the Bryants brought with them the wherewithal and gave generously to the Church and village events. Cocktail parties became the 'in' thing at Cross Cottage.

The Bryants already employed a gardener and decided they needed a 'Man Friday' to look after the house when they were away, and to do some cooking and cleaning. An advert for such a person was placed in *The Times* and resulted in several applicants. The one chosen for the post was Arthur Hobbs; his credentials were impressive. He was a captain in the Tank Corps, invalided from his regiment through injuries in Normandy; he had been decorated for bravery in front of the enemy; his father was a Baptist Minister.

Arthur Hobbs arrived, a smart young man. The Bryants fitted him out with a white jacket, and grey trousers. He did impress the cocktail folk. One thing he did tell his employer was that he would be unable to do any heavy work because of his injuries.

A garage for Mr Bryant's Daimler car had been built in the orchard and old Tom Bradfield was thatching it. Tom had served in the First World War. He didn't like the look of Hobbs. He said to me, 'You know there's something fishy about that gentleman. He doesn't look like an army officer. He's got a shifty way with him when I say Good Morning.'

Hobbs was always at the gate of the cottage when the Bryants arrived from town. He opened the gate into the garage drive, saluted his employer, then carried the shopping into the house, attentive to the extreme.

Some days Hobbs would play the Church organ and when he attended Chapel after the service he would make that organ talk too. I began to wonder whether Mr Hobbs was genuine. He would sit at the back in Chapel and take down the sermon in shorthand. I wondered why.

Francis Cambridge, a village man greatly missed in The Cuckoo Pen, was a caring man, a forgiving man, and was impressed by Hobbs. He asked him to start a club for the youth of the village. The wheels were already turning in that direction; Arthur did have a following among the village girls.

The bathroom at Cross Cottage was above average for the houses and cottages of The Cuckoo Pen. In fact, many folk still used the tin bath on a Friday night. Arthur Hobbs fancied one of the Church choir girls. He told her that Mrs Bryant had said that she was welcome to have a bath at Cross Cottage on Fridays when the Bryants were in Birmingham. Arthur looked forward to those Friday nights. He had bored a hole with an auger in one of the beams which led from the hall to the downstairs bathroom. When the girl was bathing Arthur used the spyhole. He was a twisted man, but his unpleasantness was revealed later.

Francis Cambridge suggested at the Social Centre Committee that Arthur would be a valuable member to co-opt. There was talk of a possible boy scout troop being formed in The Cuckoo Pen, with

Arthur as leader. He had been in the scouts some years back. When the District Commissioner at the nearby town was approached he made enquiries into Arthur's qualifications. He phoned Francis urgently with the news that Hobbs had been found guilty of indecent assault on small boys. Francis told Arthur about this and next morning he was gone from The Cuckoo Pen.

Mr and Mrs Bryant were in Birmingham when Arthur made his getaway. He helped himself to what cash there was around the house, took Mr Bryant's rather special camera, and all the silver he could stack into the carrier of a bicycle. The Bryant's phoned all day from Birmingham and got no reply and by the time they returned to The Cuckoo Pen Arthur had cycled away to the West Country.

He had bed and breakfast at some pub in Somerset but the police picked him up the next day. It turned out that Arthur had a conviction list as long as your arm. When he took the Man Friday job he had only just been released from Dartmoor.

I rang Mr Bryant and commiserated with him over the loss of his possessions. He said, 'That's nothing. What really upsets me is the fact that for so many years as Director of my company I've been interviewing staff and now this chap with phoney references has tricked me.'

My tractor driver always maintained that The Cuckoo Pen seemed to draw the crooked folk and it's here they would all come. That's not true of course. Con men prey on all villages and unassuming village folk.

Wartime did move folk around, and the good, the bad and the indifferent all came to The Cuckoo Pen.

At the beginning of the war one of the larger houses in The Cuckoo Pen became a home for evacuees from cities such as London and Birmingham. Joan Hitchcock, a smart Londoner, arrived. With her tweedy body, head scarf and Russian boots, she looked the part among the black and white timber houses. At this time, the WI needed a new treasurer.

'Oh, Joan, she's been a secretary in London. She would be ideal.'
So said Mrs Stone, a breeches-and-stocking, six-foot-tall market
gardener from Bachelor's Avenue. Joan took the job. She arranged a
flower show to benefit the troops, buying them luxuries with the
proceeds. But mixing sand with the sugar was her undoing. She was
discovered and did a moonlight flit from The Cuckoo Pen. Trusting
folk were hoodwinked once again.

In a little cottage on a bank overlooking the village school lived
Alice Taylor. Ever since the death of her husband, Alice gave music
lessons to the children of the village. She had a knack with children,
having been a schoolteacher before her marriage.

Alice's brother, Bob Penny, became friendly with a John Barker,
who worked in a garage in town. Bob introduced him to his sister.

This John Barker lived in digs at a pub called The Cross Keys.
Alice, a lonely soul since the death of her husband, offered John
accommodation at her cottage, which he accepted. Alice, now in her
sixties, fell hook, line and sinker for John Barker. He had a way with
women, he was smooth and patronizing.

Every evening he cycled the 5 miles from town to Alice's cottage,
where a cooked meal was ready. Classical music on radio made
evenings at Bank Cottage a delight for Alice as she and John shared
the sitting-room fire.

The discussions at Bank Cottage in the evening often turned to
religion. Alice was a devout member of the Church of England with
a great gift for music. As she played the piano in her little sitting-
room, John charmed her with his singing of the well-known hymns.
His tenor voice reminded her of her late father, William Penny.

I knew Alice Taylor's cottage very well and the sitting-room was
true Victorian: the whatnot in the corner, the glass-dropping
ornament hung on little strings which tinkled, the piano,
complete with candle holders and candles, an old gateleg table,
mahogany music stands, heaps of music, and old photographs of
the Penny family. One thing which impressed me was the big
family Bible with the names of the Penny family going way back.

The Bible was kept on an oak lectern. Alice prized that more than anything.

My daughter learned to play on Alice's piano, along with several of her cousins. Collecting them from music lessons was a treat. Alice was such a lady, and generous to the extreme. At Christmas she held parties with goodies for her pupils.

John Barker would turn the pages of the Bible, and offer to read to Alice. She thought that wonderful, and encouraged him. Every night before bedtime this man with great expression read the sacred words. Alice loved 'Songs of Solomon' and when he read those words she would imagine that the writer meant it for her.

One evening John said, 'Our boss has a decent second-hand Austin car for sale. I only wish I had the cash to buy it.'

'What a shame,' Alice replied.

Then John told her that if he had a car he would take her to places at the weekend, shopping and outings.

'How much is the car, John?' Alice enquired.

'£300, but I could knock him down to £250.'

Before the words were out of his mouth, Alice replied, 'I'll buy it for you.' John promised to pay her back when he had the money.

Life was then so exciting for Alice. Saturday afternoons were spent in Cheltenham, Gloucester, Worcester. They had tea at Cavendish House, The Cadena, Russell and Dorrels.

John Barker used to garage his car in Bob Penny's garage, a little way up The Cuckoo Pen. He knew that a new model of car was in the pipeline at Austin's Longbridge works near Birmingham.

'I've ordered the new model car and the agents are letting me have one when it comes out in three months time,' he exclaimed.

Bob and Alice were impressed and looked forward to the new car.

'There's one problem, Bob,' he said, 'Your garage will not be big enough to house the new model. It's a 2,000 cc car. Do you think we could extend your garage?'

Bob thought a while, then answered, 'I see no problem. It will take a bit off my garden but I've got too much to cultivate at my time of life.'

Every weekend for a while Bob and John were busy extending the garage with timber and roofing felt. Neighbours were curious and wondered how big this car was going to be. The garage was eventually finished, but John Barker recognized the fact that he could extract more money from the woman who loved him. So pretending to be interested in the history of the parish and in Bank Cottage in particular, he asked Alice about its history.

'The ownership does go back well into the eighteenth century,' Alice told him. 'The deeds make interesting reading.'

Here was John's opportunity. He quietly said, 'Can I have a glimpse of the deeds of Bank Cottage?'

'Of course you can, John. You are now a part of the cottage and so close to me.'

That afternoon John took the deeds to a Birmingham solicitor and obtained a substantial mortgage. Alice waited for his return, but without avail.

Next day Bob became suspicious at last and informed the police. The Austin car had been seen in Bridgwater but disappeared the next day. A message was broadcast on the radio for John Barker to return to The Cuckoo Pen where Alice Taylor was seriously ill, but this only made John think that he was a wanted man. He drove his car on to a lonely spot on Exmoor and took an overdose of drugs. He was found unconscious by the police. After hospital treatment this man who had conned Alice Taylor and persuaded Bob Penny to extend his garage was arrested. He had a long list of convictions for taking money from lonely women.

I gather from Bob that with his help, and their solicitor, Alice Taylor got back her deeds but in a short time this con man had spent a portion of the mortgage money. Alice recovered from this dreadful affair after a while and was back teaching music to the boys and girls of The Cuckoo Pen.

Bob Penny was a good friend of mine and I pulled his leg about the large garage in his garden for a car that was never going to arrive.

Bob told me that his father came from Birmingham as a gentleman's gardener to someone who bought a very nice black and white house known as The Close. The owner, whose name was well known in light industry, was also a solicitor. He used clients' money to invest in industry, was charged and sent to prison. That was a sad day for The Cuckoo Pen, for this unassuming gentleman had been held in great esteem. Mother told me that every morning she used to see him walk down the road along the Groaten to the station for his paper.

One morning two detectives were waiting. They arrested him and took him to Birmingham. He never saw The Cuckoo Pen again. He didn't actually die in prison but in the prison hospital. His rather grand grave is in The Cuckoo Pen churchyard.

But the presence of these dishonest folk doesn't mean that The Cuckoo Pen was a den of iniquity. These happenings occur up and down the length and breadth of Britain. It amounts to greed and the fact that simple country folk are more susceptible to con men and crooks. Perhaps they are just too trusting.

PEACE CELEBRATIONS

The Parish Council had decided that when peace with Germany became a reality a bonfire was to be lit by that circle of trees known as The Cuckoo Pen.

During that day in May the committee organized sports in a field known as Church Close, which lay below The Cuckoo Pen. The old games of pillow fights on a horizontal pole, blindfold wheel barrow races, and singing for a pig entertained the folk of this village. Children's races were organized by Miss Jeffreys and Cissy Tredwell, egg and spoon races and slow bicycle races. Under the great oaks of The Close trestle-tables were laden with food and drink. Where it all came from in those strict rationing days no one knew. No one asked questions. A great ham from a Gloucester Old Spot pig, donated by Laughing Tom, had been cooked by the Brawn Queen, Shoppy Bradfield. Tom's bacon and hams, wrapped in muslin, had been kept for years in his kitchen at The Croft. The ham, the eggs from Tom's flock of poultry in his orchard, boiled by the Brawn Queen, and pickles from the WI, gave a peacetime look to the plates on the tables, even though peace had only been declared for a day. Frank Bird gave a barrel of cider and Teddy Pride gave a small cask of Perry to be drunk by the bonfire later.

Revd Vernon said grace, and how he liked his food! Old Jubilee carried the hams. Two Italian prisoners, Guisseppe and Pedro, who had worked for me through the war, asked if they could join us. They asked a good question! Revd Vernon welcomed them and the two, in brown battledress, sat between Miss Jeffreys and Cissy Tredwell. Across the field in their Sunday best and wearing bowler hats came three ex-Servicemen from the First World War – Sapper, Snob and Tat Steward. They were wearing their medals and had been drinking heavily.

'Consorting with the enemy are you?' Snob said to Revd Vernon.

But the Revd replied, 'The war's over, let bygones be bygones.'

'Those two beggars should be shot,' Snob retorted.

'Oh dear. We must show tolerance to these chaps. They didn't start the war,' Miss Jeffreys interjected.

Snob's medals dangled on his chest like the martingale on a Shire horse. He showed no tolerance but told Miss Jeffreys that he was fighting the Boers before her ass was as big as a sixpence.

'That's enough of that sort of talk,' Revd Vernon said to the shoemaker, who marched off down The Close shouting, 'You are a lot of traitors!'

The cider had the opposite effect on Sapper and Tat Steward. They sang together, 'Mademoiselle from Armentières, Parlez Vous.' Then Sapper, thinking in his muddled state that the Italians should understand French, spoke the most amazing version of that language to them, ending by 'Très Bon, Vin Blanc'.

As day turned into night on that May evening Mr Cambridge's home-made paper balloon was launched. He lit the meths on the cotton wool, the balloon took shape and soon it was airborne. The folk of The Cuckoo Pen clapped and cheered as Mr Cambridge's magic balloon sailed away over the Cotswolds.

At The Manor Blenheim and Harry, Tom Dunn's men, put old Captain, the shaft horse, between the shafts of the dray and drove to the Recreation Room. Men were waiting there to load the piano. With Sacco on board the two men drove up the lane by the bakehouse on to the hill and The Cuckoo Pen. The dray was parked near the bonfire by that circle of beech trees.

The bonfire consisted of hawthorn wood from Parkers Hill where Blenheim and Harry had laid an overgrown hedge. The bonfire was built over three iron hurdles, two upright, the third forming a lintel. Tom Dunn crept inside this cavity, lit some straw, and soon the bonfire illuminated the hill and Sacco on the dray played 'Rule Britannia'.

The piano, the voices of men, women and children of The Cuckoo Pen, and the crackling of the fire, marked the end of the war. The blacked-out village of five years was over. Other bonfires along the Cotswolds answered ours at The Cuckoo Pen with a glow in the sky the children had never seen before.

Sacco's repertoire was quite amazing. He only had to hear a piece of music once and he could play it. 'Roll out the Barrel', and 'Knees up Mother Brown', he contrasted with 'The Old Rugged Cross'. His pièce de résistance was 'Jesu Joy of Man's Desiring'. Playing this puzzled him as he didn't know when to finish.

As the fire died down and midnight approached Sacco played 'God Save the King'. The peace celebrations were over.

CROSSING OVER JORDAN

A couple of lines in the hymn 'Guide me oh thou Great Jehovah' were very apt for the year after the war: 'Bear me through the swelling current, Land me safe on Canaan's side'. So many of The Cuckoo Pen hopefully 'Landed safe on Canaan's side'. Sacco, that idyllic gravedigger, had more soul, was more caring than Old Stocky had been. No clods of earth settled on the coffin when Sacco was in charge; ashes to ashes, dust to dust, was the signal for Sacco to throw some fine soil, as fine as dust, on to the deceased, like soil riddled through a fine sieve.

So often Sacco sat up all night with the dying. He would tell me he had seen them pass over Jordan. How many graves were dug that year after the war I forget. Men and women of The Cuckoo Pen had been through all the trauma of 1939–45; had tolerated the rationing, endured the black-out, said farewell to sons in the Forces, and borne the nightly drone of German bombers. They saw the victory as right triumphing over wrong. When the war ended their task was complete, so, leaving the world for others to carry on, many died, among them a lot of the characters of The Cuckoo Pen.

When Blenheim died £100 was found in his Bible, money he had saved so that he would not, as he said, be beholden to the parish. He was missed, with his peculiar walk from his arthritic limp as he drove his little herd of Shorthorns up Gipsies Lane with Brindy, the Alderney, straying under Olive's drooping ash tree.

Laughing Tom died too, after a fall. He had partly mowed his orchard with a scythe on a sunny June day. As he walked towards his house he fell, and lay there all night, a hot sultry night, unable to get on his feet. He was in hospital for a week and then Tom died.

Cow doctor, pig killer, ex-cricketer, cider maker and a man who had forgotten more of the history of The Cuckoo Pen than anyone knew, Tom could sing, tell a tale, build a rick, break in a cart-horse. In fact there was nothing which this man could not do on the farm. His skill in treating sick animals was legendary. He would boil fat bacon in cabbage water, then drench cows which had lost their cud with this revolting liquid. And it worked. He saved so many cows from choking with pieces of mangold in their gullet with his probang, a kind of ramrod, which would move the obstruction.

Sacco buried him close to scores of relatives who had lived at The Cuckoo Pen for the last 500 years. Tom's two brothers died the following winter, one a farmer, the other a tax collector and parish councillor. Sacco was busy.

Becky, Sacco's lady friend, supported the gravedigger. She plied him with cups of tea in the churchyard. Some said they made love among the graves, but Becky had a nice warm cottage to entertain the man she loved.

Tustin had lived opposite the pub but was never allowed in there by his wife Jenny. The couple lived a frugal life, scraping and scrimping, but they were happy. Jenny had saved £2,000 over the years and invested it wisely. She was a nervy little woman who talked fast and blinked behind her powerful glasses. But what a worker. After a morning as charwoman at Tom Dunn's farmhouse she climbed the high hill above The Cuckoo Pen, joined other women sprout-hoeing, spreading fertilizer, pulling charlock or anything a woman was expected to do on the land in the 1920s.

After a short illness Jenny died and poor old Tustin was devastated. She had always held the reins at Ivy Cottage. Sacco had another funeral. Tustin's daughter who lived at home accompanied the old man. She was a help to him in a way, but was mentally retarded.

The funeral was over and old Tustin sobbed his way down the churchyard, passed by the beech trees towards the lane and his cottage. Sacco, nimble as ever, sprinted after him, put his arm round him saying, 'Tustin. You should not weep, you should be shouting Hallelujah. You have been a prisoner all these years, now you're free. Come and have a drink with me tonight at the Plough and Harrow.'

Tustin, sucking his breath through his ill-fitting false teeth replied between his sobs, 'What ud the missus say?'

A few pints of cider, some tobacco in his pipe, partly compensated for the loss of Jenny. Tustin was liberated. He worked for me on the land, a useful man approaching eighty then but he lived on into his nineties.

Then Tom Dunn, the farmer, died after breaking his femur. He was missed by all. Sacco buried him next to Laughing Tom.

From the village Cross to the Chapel the apple trees were pink with blossom, the air was loud with the buzzing of the bees. Spring had come to The Cuckoo Pen. Sacco rested on his laurels after burying so many Victorians. The Brawn Queen, Shoppy Bradfield, had not been to Chapel for a while, neither had Aunt Phoebe. They were suffering a relapse from that Asian Flu. The two old friends then died the same day. Sacco was again digging the clay and stones under the hill and Revd Vernon was repeating the age-old words: 'Man that is born of woman hath but a short time to live, and is full of misery.' But Sacco and Becky didn't think so.

Sacco was kindhearted though, and this showed when he sat up night after night with Fred Hawker's wife Bertha. Yes, he saw her over Jordan. She was the last of many that Revd Vernon buried, for soon he followed his flock, clocking up 102 years.

A hard man to follow was Vernon. A Low Church man, six feet six inches tall, came to take his place. The gaunt giant of a man rode an auto-cycle, a bike with an engine on the back carrier. He didn't suit the staid members of the Church, nor the Mothers' Union. An Evangelical, he came to convert the sinners. His first mistake was to alter the form of service. He visited the non-believers and made friends with Sacco. As the worshippers left the service on Sunday mornings Revd Bruce shook hands with the folk. That was Chapel, that wasn't right. But Revd Bruce could not do anything right. The Mothers' Union did not like Mrs Bruce either, and that hat she wore!

For a while the Revd stood his ground but he had few friends among the flock. He mixed with the men on the fields and on the railway line. The Church Council did their best to get rid of him and eventually he went, and was made a Canon at a cathedral up north.

After one Sunday school outing to the seaside, when Revd Bruce was criticized for paddling in his wellington boots, Sacco summed him up in his special, literal way, 'Mr Bruce, you are despised and rejected by men. A man of sorrows and acquainted with grief.'

Revd Bruce turned to his Sexton and said, 'Sacco. You compare favourably with many so-called Christians. Your life will not go unnoticed by the One above.'

CARS AND THE WORKING MAN

After the war many changes were seen throughout society, both in rural areas and in the towns and cities. On the farming front, too, things were changing. Men from the Forces returning to The Cuckoo Pen no longer wanted to work in all weathers on low wages. They went to the engineering factories springing up in the countryside, a five-day week in temperature-controlled conditions. Young Tom Dunn, a very go-ahead farmer, bought all the new equipment available to cultivate his 250 acres. He could see the trend of things to come, concentrating on salad crops in this new age. Tom took over the role of his father as parish councillor and on the school board.

In the local towns old cars, pre-war motors, were on sale. Eager to have a means of going into town, the factory men bought the Austin 10s of the thirties, taking their families to the bright lights of town, shopping and the theatre.

Before the war folk in the village used to read a magazine called *Sunday at Home*. But Sunday was no longer spent at home in The Cuckoo Pen. The conventional Sunday dinner became a rare occurrence as families took advantage of their new-found mobility. The car in some cases even took the place of God and Chapel. Outings at the weekends meant chicken and chips or fish and chips at the seaside, and this had implications on village life.

The smallholdings at Ayles Acre became a wasteland after the death of the little master men like William Penny. Sons of the smallholders now working a five-day week at the factories no longer had an interest in the land. Men who for generations had eaten bread, cheese and onions, now became venturesome, sampling scampi, pizzas, chilli con carni, and chips with everything. Who would be seen drinking rough cider when the whole family could go to the pub and ask for drinks like Dubonnet, gin and tonic, and Snowballs.

Tom Dunn realized that the Sunday dinner was not the feast it had been and that all over the country the cooking of meat and two veg had declined. The new generation required salads and somewhat exotic French dishes. Tom's spring onions grew all the year round though. Herbs were needed for stuffing the oven-ready chickens and the modern fast foods. Tom planted acres of parsley and sage for drying. These were labour-intensive crops, and so Tom innovated labour-saving devices. He cut the parsley and sage with a flail-mower, which was originally developed for mowing silage.

Tom moved fast when he had to make a decision. The acres of fruit became a worry to him. No one apart from the gipsies or travellers were willing to pick his plums, but the travellers wanted more money to pick the fruit than the merchants could pay for the crop. Gluts were common with fruit and vegetables; for two years Tom ploughed in crops of leeks.

So Tom pushed the fruit trees out of the ground with bulldozers, planted the land with wheat and barley, bought Hereford cattle to produce beef. Blossom Sunday, when the folk from the city came, was a memory.

Important changes also came to The Cuckoo Pen with the advent of television. The local football team struggled for support when the professional game could be seen in the comfort of home, and with the car, first division matches were in reach of The Cuckoo Pen.

Cricket under the captaincy of the Colonel had been a truly rural affair. A corrugated iron shed served for a pavilion and cowpats made the middling pitch with its wet outfield rather hazardous near the boundary.

Men from the village short of clothing coupons played in grey flannels, and one chap with a belt and braces! But this was all to change too. The rule agreed by the Colonel was that the team should consist of players from the village. When the new pavilion with showers was built, the teams joined a league playing for cups. Bowlers and batsmen from away were imported, and the emphasis was put on winning. The Colonel used to say 'I'm not interested only in winning. I want to play the game of cricket.' It was happening everywhere. The slogging strokes of villagers changed to the careful batting of a new generation, when averages were all important and the fun game became very 'respectable'.

The Recreation Room at The Cuckoo Pen had an interesting history. On winter evenings young men played billiards on a full-sized table. Social evenings were held by the Chapel folk. There were teas, suppers, magic lantern shows, political meetings, whist drives and so on. Wedding receptions could be held there, providing there was no alcohol. That was a rule of the Trustees.

Memorable pantomimes at Christmas played to a full audience. They were fun, not because of their professionalism, but because of the lack of it. 'Dick Whittington' with Madge as the cat was a classic. As pussy hopped around, Mrs Beddows' infectious belly-laugh was worth the evening out. She had noticed something wrong, and in a stage whisper said, 'I can see Madge's knickers.'

And what a stage! It was made up of the billiard table and some trestle-tables. It seemed a bit unsteady under the Alladin lamps. The curtains too; they rarely opened and closed at the right time, despite the tugging of little Teddy Pride. Cissy Tredwell the prompter had the hardest job. When she did speak from her script, there was an aggravated tone to her voice, as if to say, 'I'm fed up. Why don't you learn your lines.'

The days of the Recreation Room were numbered when the new joint village hall and school hall was built. When it went a bit of history went with it. Under the steps, where a group of whist players drank their liquid refreshment on whist drive nights during the interval, beer bottles galore were found with strange sounding names. These were the names of brewers long since gone, and a record of what the whist drive men drank on the steps of what was called the vestibule.

A heavy lead water tank on a wooden frame had stood over the ladies' powder room. It filled with water from the spoutings when it rained, and flushed the very prehistoric WC. The men had to make themselves comfortable in a semi-circle of corrugated iron sheets.

The roof of the Room had been made watertight with tarred felt. When it leaked Tom Dunn bought some corrugated iron sheets from Taffy Johns of the Army and Navy Stores. He bought it cheap to cover the room. These sheets had been salvaged from the English Channel when the cargo boat carrying them had been sunk by a German U-boat. They were very rough but with a coating of tar they kept the folk dry in the Recreation Room below.

The new school and village hall combined was so different from the old Recreation Room. It had a very good kitchen, cloakrooms, and a stage which would have compared quite well with that of a theatre. The central heating was a far cry from the old coke stove.

Apart from these improvements to social life in The Cuckoo Pen, a senior school was being built in Townsend Piece, a field of heavy clay on the outskirts of the village. Why it was planned several stories high is a good question. Townsend Piece was bought from a good farmer at agricultural land price, for, being outside the village it was not considered building land and was therefore cheap. However, the school drew many comments from the local folk; some said it looked like a biscuit factory.

One teacher who came to The Cuckoo Pen and gave the pupils a grounding in history was also a producer of plays and he started a dramatic society at the new social centre. Ned Gold worked hard with amateur material to get his actors and actresses into shape. Times had changed. Madge as the cat in 'Dick Whittington' would not do. Ned had to compete with the television. His productions had to be near perfect. Late into the night Ned thrashed his cast until the opening night and one must admit the result was a credit to the village. In fact, it would have been a credit to any town production. Folk did go in their cars to the theatres in Birmingham, Coventry, Bristol, but Ned Gold did a good job teaching folk to have a go themselves.